HERMAN BURSTEIN

stereo

...HOW IT WORKS

GERNSBACK LIBRARY, Inc.
NEW YORK 11, N. Y.

contents

introduction

HIGH fidelity is part attainment and part quest. While modern audio techniques and equipment make it possible to enjoy very good reproduction of sound, it cannot be said that the art is yet capable of achieving an exact facsimile, indistinguishable from the original for all listeners. This shortcoming is particularly apparent when a large group such as a symphony is concerned. Thus the quest continues for a faithful imitation of the live performance. Every year produces developments that bring us closer to the elusive goal of perfect reproduction, a goal that many find eminently worth pursuing even though it may never be reached.

Stereophonic reproduction looms large as a means toward the objective of complete realism. At this writing, the seed which was sown more than 25 years ago is just beginning to bear fruit. Stereophonic components for the home—stereo cartridges, stereo control amplifiers, stereo integrated amplifiers, dual speaker systems, dual FM–AM tuners (that can be operated simultaneously), multiplex adapters, stereo tape recorders, etc.—are all of quite recent vintage. The stereo disc is just making headway. Stereo tapes, although on the scene for a while, are still relatively costly and have not yet appreciably tapped their estimated potential. All in all, stereo in the home is very young.

But, to place the stereo art in proper perspective, it is well to realize that its history goes back more than a quarter of a century. Among the notable highlights of this history are the experiments conducted at the American Academy of Music in Philadelphia in 1932: a tailor's dummy named Oscar, with a microphone in each ear, was used to pick up various sounds emanating from the stage of the auditorium. The sounds received by the left and right microphones were amplified and fed, respectively, to the left and right sides of earphones worn by listeners in various parts of the auditorium.

Through Oscar, an appreciable segment of the public made its first acquaintance with stereophonic reproduction at the Century of Progress Exposition in Chicago in 1933. Oscar was placed in a booth and visitors who stepped up to a nearby balcony and donned earphones were able to listen in binaural fashion, through Oscar's ears, to the various sounds in his vicinity.

In 1933, Bell Laboratories conducted a series of experiments to determine the extent to which listeners could identify the original location of a sound. Two or three microphones in various arrangements were used with two or three speakers. The sound source and microphones were in an acoustically treated room, while the speakers were on the stage of an auditorium and concealed behind a curtain.

On April 27, 1933, the performance of the Philadelphia Orchestra at the American Academy of Music in Philadelphia was picked up by two microphones at each end of the stage and transmitted by telephone cable to loudspeakers on the stage of Constitution Hall in Washington, D. C. On that pioneer occasion, Dr. F. B. Jewett, vice president of the American Telephone & Telegraph Co. commented:

> "As to the future of the accomplishment shown here today, it is difficult to make any definite prediction. What we have done is to produce pickup microphones, amplifiers, electrical filters, transmission lines and loudspeaking reproducers so perfect that the entire frequency and volume range of the most exacting orchestral and vocal music can be reproduced at a distance without impairment of quality. We have also worked out the arrangements by which substantially perfect auditory perspective is possible. This latter is an essential part of the problem if realistic illusion as to the physical arrangement of the component parts of an orchestra is desired.
>
> We can place at the disposal of the musical director instrumentalities which will enable him to produce at a distant point, or at many distant points simultaneously, a completely faithful replica of the tonal effects produced locally in the auditorium on the stage of which the orchestra is performing . . ."[1]

Why did it take stereophonic reproduction, proved successful at least as far back as 1933, a quarter of a century to make its

[1] "The Reproduction of Orchestral Music in Auditory Perspective," *Bell Laboratories Record,* May, 1933.

appearance in the home? For one thing, there was the problem of a satisfactory medium of transmission. The experiments in the 1930's used telephone lines as the link between the microphones and the earphones or loudspeakers. While suitable for demonstration and experimental purposes, telephone lines are not economically satisfactory as a stereo link to the home. Today, however, we have three satisfactory media—radio, phonograph and tape—capable of bringing into the home high quality sound. Each offers wide and uniform frequency response, low distortion and low noise. Radio and the phonograph as they existed in 1933 did not provide high-quality transmission; and tape did not yet exist in a commercial, practical sense. Improvements in radio have included developments both in transmission and reception, with particular emphasis on FM. In the case of the phonograph, great technical progress has been made in cutting machines, recording techniques, disc material, speeds, turntables, cartridges and tone arms.

Another factor in the delayed appearance of stereo in the home is the transition from the laboratory to the consumer—generally a long and difficult process. The development of a new art or science is never smooth but strewn with pitfalls and setbacks. There are inevitably conflicts of theory and opinion to be reconciled, and agreements to be reached with respect to technology so that the public is presented with one basic system and not with a number of systems among which it must choose without knowing how to choose. As cases in point, there is quite general agreement that the Westrex system is to be used for phonograph discs; that stacked rather than staggered heads are to be used for tape; that NARTB equalization shall be used for tape.

Finally, the public must want and be ready for the new technology. A product can be ahead of its time and fail for that reason only, not because of its technical shortcomings. Over the past decade, high fidelity has been developing from what some persons termed a fad into a permanent part of our way of life, much as the electric refrigerator, the TV set and similar items have become part of our fabric of living. Thus a firm foundation has been built up for the introduction of stereo. Having grown aware of and accustomed to the opportunities for good reproduction of music, the public next wants better and better reproduction—it seems to be a basic law that our wants are never satiated. And so the time is ripe for stereo. While stereo is sufficiently advanced to have made the transition from the laboratory to the home and to increase measurably the pleasure derived by many persons from reproduced music, far from enough is yet known as to the best techniques and the best types of equipment. Microphone placement, types of microphones to be used, broadcasting and recording techniques, functions and controls required of stereo amplifiers, types of speakers, speaker placement, etc., are all areas open to further thought, research and experiment. Hence the stereo art must be recognized for what it is—a rapidly growing infant.

Therefore, it is not possible at this time to present the reader with a book containing nothing but incontrovertible facts on stereo. He is entitled, however, to the benefit of expert opinion on what constitutes good stereo. Admittedly, some of the expert opinions of a few years ago, or even a few months ago, have already been cast under doubt. That is inevitable in so new a field. Doubtless some of the viewpoints presented will similarly be subjected to re-evaluation in the future. On the other hand, the art has developed sufficiently along both theoretical and empirical lines so that a book can now be written that contains enough useful information to be worth while. If the experts are guessing, at least their guesses are well-informed ones and more apt to prove right than wrong.

This book seeks to be objective about stereo rather than to eulogize it. Therefore it will be concerned with problems as well as techniques and rewards. While stereo has much to offer, it is not a miracle of some sort which in a moment makes everything monophonic obsolete and conquers all previous problems of audio reproduction. While stereo can add something of value to audio reproduction that has already achieved a high degree of quality, it cannot mask serious faults. Moreover, while stereo has something to give, it is also apt to demand something in return, such as greater outlay of funds, more patience, more effort and more space than usually required for mono reproduction.

This book is written as much for the nontechnical audiophile as for the individual versed in electronic lore. It is assumed only that the reader has a rudimentary acquaintance with the parlance of high fidelity, so that it is not necessary to explain to him such terms as amplifier, preamplifier, tuner, cartridge, woofer, tweeter, frequency response, distortion, signal-to-noise ratio, etc. Those who would like a primer on high fidelity are referred to the author's book, *Fundamentals of High Fidelity*.[2]

While most audiophiles are concerned principally with the

---

[2] John F. Rider, Publisher, Inc.

problems of setting up a stereo system in the home and of obtaining maximum performance from this equipment, the author feels that a well-rounded knowledge of stereo, including the recording and broadcasting aspects, is of value to the reader. Therefore, this book is concerned not only with the playback aspect of stereo but also with the techniques of microphoning it over the air. Such background of fundamentals enables the audiophile to have a better concept of what is required of his playback equipment. Furthermore, there are principles at work in the recording and broadcasting phases that have counterparts in the playback aspect. Finally, it is hoped that a full account of the stereo art will help satisfy intellectual curiosity.

If one's demands and tastes are moderate, the stereo equipment initially acquired is apt to be satisfactory for a substantial period of time. But if one's demands are exacting, the stereo art after a few years will offer much more than at the outset. However, this should not prove a deterrent, at least not to the audiophile with something of the pioneering spirit who desires the thrill of close contact with a burgeoning art, the same thrill that was experienced by those who kept in close touch with the early years of radio and of television. Moreover, such equipment changes as may be dictated by improvements in the art will probably be piecemeal ones, necessitating the replacement of one component at a time rather than of the entire system at once. This is a pattern familiar in monophonic reproduction; we have obtained a better amplifier at one time, a better cartridge at another and so on. The components that were replaced were not necessarily thrown out, but either traded in for the new ones or used for a second high-fidelity system, for example, in the den or workshop.

The author would like to express his appreciation to the editors of *Radio & TV News* for permission to use materials from a number of articles on stereo that he has written for that periodical. Thanks are similarly due to *Electronic Technician* and RADIO-ELECTRONICS Magazine for permission to use portions of articles appearing in those magazines.

HERMAN BURSTEIN

forms of audio reproduction

To view stereo in its proper context we must understand the differences between stereo and conventional high fidelity as well as the things they have in common.

A basic distinction is simply that between monophonic and non-monophonic sound. The latter breaks down into three classifications: binaural, stereo and a mid-way category, quasi-stereo.

In discussing these categories you will find the word *channel* recurrent. Channel signifies a device or a technique for conveying one audio signal during recording, transmission or reproduction of sound. This one signal can be very complex, for example, representing a large number of instruments or a group of voices. Channel also refers to the audio signal so conveyed. Thus, we may be referring to a group of related components in a disc or tape recording studio or in a broadcast studio; to a group of audio components in the home; to a waveform physically inscribed on a record, magnetically inscribed on tape, electromagnetically propagated via a radio wave; to the sound itself as it greets the ear.

Where more than one channel is used, as in binaural and stereo reproduction, and the reference is to the signal or sound, one channel is distinguished from the other by differences in one, several or all of the following characteristics: frequencies (produced by various sound sources) appearing in each signal; overall loudness; relative amplitudes of various frequencies; time delay; phase (portion of the cycle at a given instant, corresponding to compression or rarefaction of the air, as shown in Fig. 101); ratio of reverberated sound (reflected from room surfaces and objects) to direct sound.

Monophonic sound

Until the advent of stereo, high fidelity was customarily associated (Fig. 102) with a single chain of elements—or channel—con-

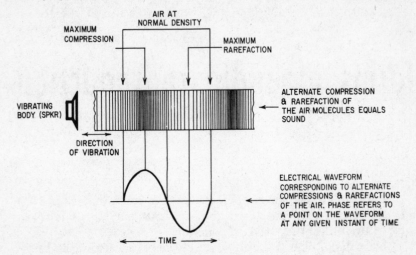

Fig. 101. *Phase of a sound wave.*

sisting of the following: a program source, which could be a radio or TV station, phono disc, or recorded tape; a signal source, which

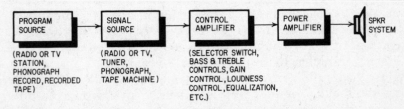

Fig. 102. *Basic elements of a monophonic system.*

could be a tuner (including TV sound), phonograph or tape play-back machine; a control amplifier, containing gain, bass, treble, selection, etc., controls; a power amplifier and a speaker system.

Strictly speaking, the term monaural means one-eared. Application of this term to single-channel sound is disturbing to the semanticist, and the word *monophonic* has been coined to represent audio reproduction via one signal and one group of components. It is a more precise term and therefore will be used instead of the word monaural.

Binaural reproduction

The first form of non-monophonic sound intended for the home market was binaural; a two-channel system designed for use with earphones. Binaural sound was made available to the public in the early 1950's and was predicated on the use of a tape playback machine.

In recording, two microphones are placed approximately 6 to

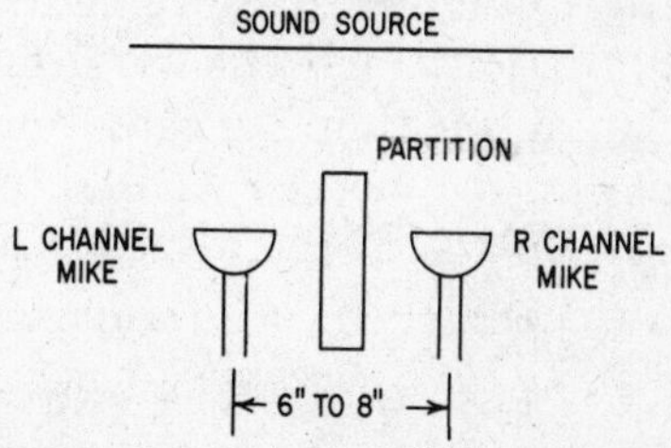

Fig. 103. *Microphones for binaural recording.*

8 inches apart—about the same distance as between human ears—with an intervening block or partition to simulate the obstruction caused by the head (Fig. 103). The aim is to pick up sound just as one would hear it at a live performance.

The sound reaching each microphone is converted into an electrical signal, which is recorded on a specific half of a magnetic tape (Fig. 104). The signal from the left microphone is fed to a tape head that records on the upper half of the tape, while the right microphone feeds a head that records on the lower half, assuming the tape travels from left to right.

When the tape is played back, each track is scanned by a separate head. The signal from one playback head goes to an amplifier

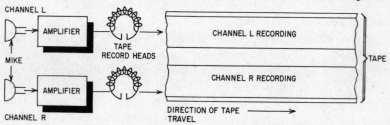

Fig. 104. *Two-channel tape recording (binaural or stereo).*

(which supplies correct playback equalization) and from there to the left earphone. The signal from the other head goes to a separate amplifier and thence to the right earphone (Fig. 105).

The signal and equipment for the left ear are customarily referred to as channel 1 or A or L; for the right ear as channel 2 or

13

B or R. We shall use the terms channel L and channel R, because they leave no doubt as to whether the reference is to the left or right microphone, speaker or associated equipment.

Results achieved by the binaural method have been acclaimed as astonishingly realistic. However, the system has not attained a wide degree of acceptance because of the discomfort and inconvenience of the earphones. They literally chain the listener, limiting his range of movement. True, some individuals accept the limitations in exchange for the spaciousness and realism of binaural listening. But most music lovers feel the price is too great to pay for the increase in listening pleasure. Too, frequency response, particularly at the low end, is not as good with earphones as with

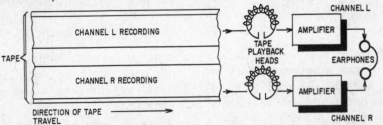

Fig. 105. *Binaural playback by means of tape.*

speakers, and good earphones are expensive. Consequently binaural reproduction, for all of its amazingly realistic effect, is seldom used for high-fidelity purposes. However, as a parenthetical note, it may be observed that the binaural technique, because of its ability to reproduce sound faithfully, has found considerable industrial use as a tool for recording and analyzing sounds.

Stereophonic reproduction

Stereophonic sound is essentially identified with the arrangement of Fig. 106, employing two sound channels, with each channel having somewhat different characteristics from the other. As shown, two microphones, by virtue of their location, orientation and pickup pattern, produce different electrical signals, which are separately recorded on tape or disc or transmitted over the air. Usually, though not always, the microphones are spaced a number of feet apart, instead of inches as in binaural reproduction. In the home, the two signals are fed to a pair of amplifiers, each connected to a speaker system.

Microphone and speaker placement and the manner in which the two amplifiers are operated have a great deal to do with the extent to which the quality of sound is enhanced as compared with monophonic reproduction. That is, we must differentiate between stereo as a technique and as an effect. The technique refers to the manner in which equipment is used; the effect refers to whether we have achieved greater realism or some other pleasure-giving quality.

The system portrayed in Fig. 106 is the two-channel method, which has become synonymous with the term stereo. Actually, stereo embraces a variety of systems employing more than one

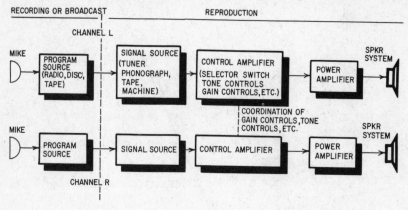

Fig. 106. *Basic elements of a stereo system.*

channel. However, when we do not specifically designate the number of channels it is understood that the reference is to the two-channel kind.

So far as home reproduction is concerned, two-channel stereo is by far the most popular and practical of the multi-channel systems. On the other hand, it is important to recognize that stereo employing more than two channels does exist, as in motion-picture theaters, and that these forms provide standards of achievement which two-channel stereo is trying to emulate. Early experiments showed that a very definite sensation of directionality and spaciousness could be had by employing a substantial number of microphones in a line parallel with the sound source, with each microphone feeding a corresponding amplifier–speaker combination (Fig. 107). This is referred to as the *curtain-of-sound* principle. The assumption is that each microphone picks up the sound in a narrow area before it, and the speaker connected to it (through a power amplifier) disperses the sound in the same radiation pattern as the pickup pattern of the microphone. Thus if a microphone picks up sound within a 45° angle, then the speaker should

15

similarly disperse the sound within a 45° angle, as shown in Fig. 108. In this way a row of microphone–amplifier–speaker chains reproduces all the sound from left to right.

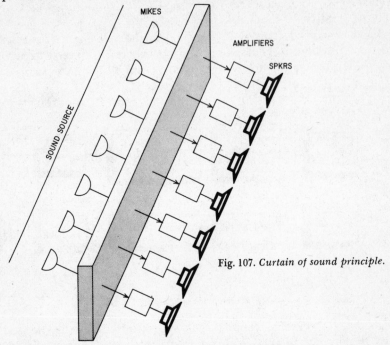

Fig. 107. *Curtain of sound principle.*

The curtain-of-sound principle has definite limitations. One is that it is difficult to find microphones and speakers having the same pickup and radiation patterns; another is that the microphones pick up reflected as well as direct sound. Nevertheless, it was found that a substantial number of microphone–speaker pairs, say six, gave very good results with respect to directionality.

The use of as many as six, or even more channels is not too serious an obstacle for the laboratory or the theater, but is out of the question for home use. Further experiments demonstrated that very little is lost in terms of directionality if the number of channels is reduced to three.

However, upon reducing the channels from three to two, the sensation of directionality diminishes sharply. Although two-channel sound is considered preferable to monophonic, it is inferior to systems employing three or more. Since two channels are the practical maximum for mass use in the light of present technology, a large amount of research has been conducted into means of obtaining results from two-channel sound virtually as good as from three-channel stereo.

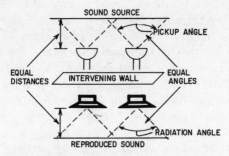

Fig. 108. *Dependence of curtain of sound principle upon correspondence between microphone pickup patterns and speaker radiation patterns.*

There is considerable evidence that with proper types and placement of microphones, as well as proper speaker placement,

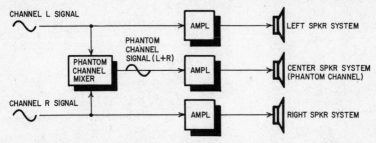

Fig. 109. *Use of a phantom channel.*

two-channel stereo can closely approach the three-channel kind. If reproduction takes place in a relatively small area, such as a typical living room rather than a comparatively large hall, the possibilities are that two-channel stereo will sound nearly as good as three-channel.

Thus, a report on stereo experiments involving a symphony orchestra had this to say:

"It could not be doubted that the three-channel system produced reproduction more nearly resembling the live original than did two-channel transmission. It is of especial interest, however, that the three-channel tapes, upon review in a much smaller auditorium of nearly ideal acoustic characteristics, could be shown to have negligible advantage over two-channel tapes."[1]

---

[1] Walter T. Selsted and Ross H. Snyder, "Acoustical and Electrical Considerations in Symphony Orchestra Reproduction," *Audio,* January, 1957.

"Hole-in-the-center" effect

One of the principal factors accounting for the difference between two- and three-channel stereo is the "hole in the center," which refers to the seeming insufficiency or total absence of sound in the space between the left and right speakers. The larger the listening room, the greater the spacing between the left and right speakers and, therefore, for a listener sitting not very far from the speakers, the more pronounced is the hole in the center. In the case of an orchestral composition, it might sound as though the left and right halves of the orchestra had been cut in two and moved a fair distance apart.

The effect can be due to excessive spacing between microphones during the recording session, to the spacing between speakers (*taking into account where the listener sits*), or to a combination of

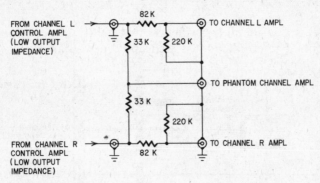

Fig. 110. *A mixer circuit for phantom channel signal.*

both. Two-channel stereo more closely approaches the quality of three-channel in smaller rooms, and one of the reasons is that the distance between speakers is likely to be less in such rooms.

In recording, use of a center microphone can help mitigate the hole-in-the-center effect. Means whereby the listener can deal with this effect are discussed in the next three sections.

Phantom channel

One solution to the hole-in-the-center problem, as proposed by Paul Klipsch,[2] is to reconstruct a center channel in playback by feeding the sound of the left and right channels to a center speaker, as shown in Fig. 109. The signal of channel L and that of channel R enter a mixing device which combines the two signals and sends them to a third amplifier which drives the center speaker. Best re-

---

[2] Paul W. Klipsch, "Two-Track, Three-Channel Stereo," *Audiocraft*, November, 1957.

sults are obtained if the levels of the L and R speakers are set so that each is 3 db below (half the power of) the center speaker when the same signal is fed to all three; thus the combined power of the L and R speakers equals that of the center speaker; Fig. 110 is a mixing circuit suggested by Klipsch. However, the audiophile seeking to experiment along the lines of a phantom channel might very well, after first balancing the L and R speakers for equal sound, gradually bring up the volume of the center speaker until his ears inform him that he has adequately filled the hole in the center, if any.

Dummy speaker

This expedient for filling the hole in the center has been used successfully and affords a good illustration of the importance of

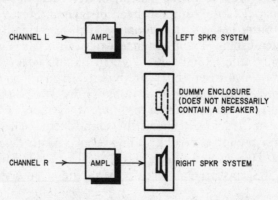

Fig. 111. *Use of a dummy speaker system.*

illusion in audio reproduction. The dummy speaker is an enclosure that apparently contains a speaker (whether it actually does is unimportant) but is not connected to anything (Fig. 111). It is placed between the left and right speakers. Because the eyes see a speaker in the center, they help persuade the ears that sound is coming from that region.

If it is hard to believe that the eyes can trick the ears in such a manner, remember that visual–aural effects are constantly used in outdoor movies. The screen is many yards in front of the viewer, while the tiny speaker is a few inches to his left or right. Yet after a few moments he is no longer conscious of the separation of sight and sound. More, should he see an orchestra or band on the screen, he will be convinced he is hearing exactly that, despite the fact that the source is a small, often metallic-sounding speaker. If he closes his eyes for a few moments, then he will again become aware of the nature, location and imperfections of the sound source.

Speaker concealment

Because of the correlation between what we see and what we hear, the hole-in-the-center effect may be partly attributed to the fact that we see two speakers spaced a substantial distance apart. The effect can be dissipated by concealing the speakers behind a curtain sufficiently transparent to sound so as not to attenuate the high frequencies, but able to conceal the speakers. Proper room lighting plays a role in this.

Quasi-stereo

A number of efforts have been made, with varying degrees of success, to obtain some of the benefits of stereophonic sound, using only one signal as the source instead of several. Stereo sound has other attributes besides directionality, such as a quality of largeness or spaciousness. These characteristics can be duplicated without the effort and expense involved in having two channels for recording, transmitting and reproducing. In fact, some methods have attempted to impart directionality by allocating different portions of the audio spectrum to different speakers or by causing differences in the arrival time of the sound from each speaker.

The term pseudo-stereo has often been used to describe these techniques. However, the term has a rather disparaging connotation, and it seems preferable to refer to these methods as quasi-stereo.

For some, quasi-stereo may be a stepping stone toward true stereo. For others, it may prove that there is nothing like true stereo. And for still others, it may be a quite satisfactory stopping point.

Multiple speakers

Probably the simplest of the quasi-stereo techniques is to connect two (or more) speaker systems to the power amplifier and to space the speakers several feet apart (Fig. 112). If the music was originally performed by an ensemble occupying a substantial amount of space, as by an orchestra or glee club, greater realism and enhanced listening pleasure can be obtained by having a broad sound source as contrasted with the narrow distribution afforded by a single speaker system.

On the other hand, particularly where just two speaker systems are employed, there may be difficulty in the reproduction of a solo voice or instrument. Although in theory the sound should appear to come from a point between the two speakers, in actuality the listener may be quite conscious of, and disturbed by, the same sound coming from two points in the room. True stereo minimizes this by assigning the solo voice or instrument entirely or largely to one of the channels. On the other hand, if three speakers are employed for quasi-stereo, and particularly if the highest volume level is assigned to the center one, the illusion of the soloist being in the center would be fortified.

Some authorities believe that best results are obtained with the multiple-speaker approach when the speakers have unlike

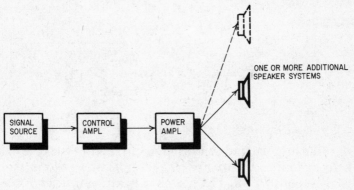

Fig. 112. *Quasi-stereo based on use of multiple speaker systems.*

characteristics. No speaker system yet developed is perfectly smooth. If it stays within + 4db (loudness variation of 150%) between 40 and 15,000 cycles, it can be considered excellent. Thus every speaker system has peaks at which certain frequencies are exaggerated and dips at which others are attenuated. These peaks and dips, particularly the peaks, in large part account for the characteristic, identifying quality of a speaker system. So long as we have to live with imperfect speakers, it is felt by some that use of two different ones will result in emphasis of different instruments by each speaker, which may help impart a feeling of separation of instruments, such as is associated with true stereo. On the other hand, since most instruments have a fairly wide frequency range, a given instrument may appear to change its location from one side of the room to the other as various parts of the scale are played.

Another and perhaps more convincing argument in behalf of dissimilar speakers for quasi-stereo is that each speaker will provide a different impression of the total sound. Thus the ears receive versions of the same thing, which blend in the mind to produce a fuller, rounder effect than if both speakers produced exactly the same acoustic waveform.

Acoustic delay

At least one device on the market, appearing under the name Xophonic, seeks to imitate the spaciousness of stereo sound by supplying something akin to an echo, but with a smaller time lag

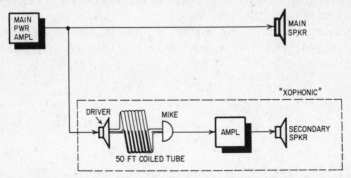

Fig. 113. *Quasi-stereo system employing the Xophonic unit.*

between the original and following sound than in the case of true echo. It is more in the nature of a reverberation, except that the original sound is followed by just one repetition instead of a series.

Fig. 113 shows how the Xophonic device operates. The signal from the main power amplifier is fed into the driver, a small speaker. The sound produced goes into a coiled tube tightly coupled (no air leaks) to it. The coiled tube has a total length of about 50 feet. Since sound travels slightly more than 1 foot per millisecond, it takes about one-twentieth of a second for the sound to emerge from the other end of the tube. There it actuates a microphone, tightly coupled to the tube. The resulting electrical signal produced by the microphone goes to a second power amplifier and speaker, both contained in the Xophonic unit. The second speaker reproduces the original signal with a delay of about one-twentieth of a second.

The frequency range of the Xophonic is fairly limited, about 200 to 3,000 cycles. On the other hand, it is intended for operation at a level substantially below that of the main speaker system, so that its limited range does not color the overall sound. The level of the secondary speaker is set by increasing the gain of the Xophonic amplifier until the reverberated sound becomes just noticeable. It is claimed that location of the Xophonic speaker is not critical with respect to the principal speaker system.

The effectiveness of a time-delay device depends upon the amount of reverberation already present in a program source and upon the listening room. If the program material contains substantial reverberation (due either to the characteristics of the original performance site or to reverberation electrically or acoustically supplied afterward by the engineers at the recording studio)

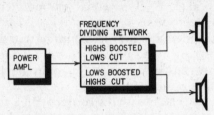

Fig. 114. *Quasi-stereo based on frequency division.*

any additional effects may prove more annoying than gratifying. Added reverberation may also be unwanted if the listening room is live and produces reverberation of its own. If the program material has a "dry" quality and the listening room has soft furnishings, such as drapes, heavy carpeting and upholstered furniture (which tend to absorb the sound) added reverberation may appreciably increase one's listening pleasure.

Following is the manufacturer's description of tests comparing a stereo system with the Xophonic device:

"An . . . A–B comparison between a system providing location effect and an Xophonic system was made in our sound laboratories. A two-channel recording was used as the source material in the A-position of the comparison switch, and this was reproduced through a pair of identical amplifiers into two matching speakers. The placement of the speakers was carefully chosen to provide the best feeling of orchestral location. In the B-switch position, the two original channels were mixed to provide the normal monaural [monophonic] source. This was reproduced in one of the speakers, and also by the Xophonic. In this way, an immediate-comparison A–B test was made between a two-channel system and Xophonic sound.

The result of the comparison was as follows: . . . 94% (of the listeners) were able to differentiate between the location effect and the reverberation effect of Xophonic reproduction. What was significant was that . . . 65% of the listeners actually preferred the reverberation effect to the location effect of the two-channel system."[3]

---

[3] "A Reverberation Unit for Hi-Fi Reproduction," *Radio & TV News*, June, 1957.

Frequency division

Here we have a quasi-stereo technique that feeds preponderantly high frequencies to one speaker and low ones to the other (Fig. 114). A special network following the power amplifier attenuates the low frequencies and emphasizes the high frequencies for the left speaker, while the lows are boosted and the highs cut for the right speaker. A commercial embodiment of this technique is the CBS XD Sound System.

Following is the manufacturer's account of tests comparing three sets of conditions, involving two stereo sound tracks on tape and three speakers, two in the corners of a room along the same wall and the third at the center of the wall:

"*Condition 1.* The two tracks corresponding to the left and right microphones were electrically combined and fed directly to the center speaker. This was equivalent to conventional single-speaker sound reproduction.

Condition 2. The left sound track was fed to the speaker in the left corner and the right track to the speaker in the right corner. This system corresponded to true stereophonic reproduction.

Condition 3. The two tracks were again electrically combined as under condition 1, but before the resultant signal reached the left speaker, it passed through an equalizing circuit which attenuated the lows and emphasized the high frequencies. The right speaker also received the combined signal, but through an equalizer which attenuated the highs and emphasized the lows.

Listeners were invited to these tests without being told what the conditions were. They were asked to express their preferences of sound reproduction by choosing from any one of the three conditions. The result of the study was startling but in some respects not unexpected. While not a single listener (about a total of 50 were exposed) preferred condition 1—that is, the single conventional speaker—their preferences were almost equally divided between conditions 2 and 3. Evidently, the simulated stereophonic sound seemed to give as much satisfaction as the true one. As a matter of fact, when people began to wander around the room, more listeners preferred the simulated stereophonic rendition (condition 3) because it seemed to give satisfactory results over a less restricted area than the true stereophonic sound.

A variation of these tests was performed on a number of listeners who were technically or musically well informed on the state of the stereophonic art. These listeners were told what the three conditions corresponded to and were asked to determine which condition, 2 or 3, represented the true stereophonic rendition. Half of them guessed right and half of them guessed wrong, again proving that true stereophonic rendition can be successfully simulated with a single source of program."[4]

Coded stereo

Known as Perspecta Sound in one of its commercial forms, coded stereo comes closest to true stereo in terms of directionality. As in Fig. 115, three or more speakers are customarily used, each

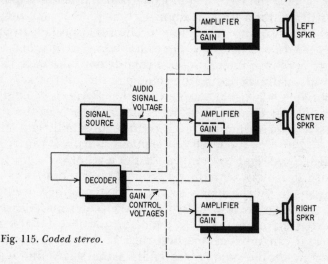

Fig. 115. *Coded stereo.*

driven by its own power amplifier. All the power amplifiers receive the same signal, but operate at different volume levels as determined by code signals—one for each amplifier—that accompany the audio signal. The code signals are detected by a special unit,

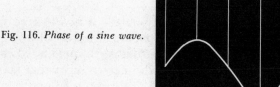

Fig. 116. *Phase of a sine wave.*

which controls the gain of each power amplifier. While Fig. 115 shows three speakers, a greater number could be used.

The code signals must be inaudible and therefore have to be kept outside the audio range, either below 30 or above 20,000

---

[4] Peter C. Goldmark, "The Columbia XD (Extra-Dimensional) Sound System," *Audio,* October, 1953.

cycles. Usually they consist of the extremely low frequencies because of the technical problems associated with ultrasonic tones, which are much more easily lost on such media as tape and film than are the subaudible notes.

By means of coded stereo, the *total* sound can be made to appear as though it originates from the left, center, right or intermediate points. During the recording process, trained personnel apply code signals to the recording medium, such as tape or motion-picture film, thereby varying the volume levels of the speakers to produce the desired directional effect. For example, a marching band can be made to appear as though it were coming onto the stage from the left by gradually increasing the volume of the left speaker (via the appropriate code signal), while the other speakers remain silent. The band can be moved to the center and then to the right by successively increasing the levels of the center and right speakers, while diminishing the levels of the others. Finally it can be moved off stage to the right by diminishing the level of the right speaker.

Coded stereo can reproduce a game of table tennis as effectively as true stereo by alternately switching between the left and right speakers, with an occasional switch to the center speaker when the ball drops at the net. Or, by reducing the level of the middle speaker, it can produce an effect such as that of two trumpeters playing *in unison* at opposite ends of the stage. But it cannot *simultaneously* reproduce different instruments playing at the left, center and right so that each instrument can be identified as coming from the appropriate direction. Nevertheless, with skilled use of the code signals to achieve appropriate shifts of the total sound, impressive effects can be achieved.

Coded stereo has been used for motion pictures.

Phase shift

Several devices on the market achieve a quasi-stereo effect by changing the phase of the monophonic signal as of any given instant and sending the phase-shifted signal through a second amplifier and speaker system. Thus, the ears receive two versions of the same signal, which may blend in the mind to produce a fuller image of the sound. The phase-shift devices do not operate uniformly at all frequencies. As a result, the phase relationship between the fundamental frequency and its harmonics is altered by the phase-shift network. This produces a difference in waveform between the main and secondary speakers, thereby further increasing the difference between the sounds of the two speakers.

If the device can achieve sufficient phase shift—slowing all or some of the frequencies by a substantial part of a cycle or by several cycles—then there may be enough difference in the arrival time of the sound from the secondary speaker to produce an effect akin to reverberation.

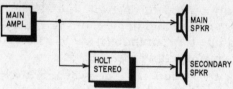

Fig. 117. *Incorporation of the Holt phase-shift unit into an audio system.*

The devices referred to effect a phase shift by electrical networks. From the beginning to the end of a cycle (Fig. 116) is 360°. Phase

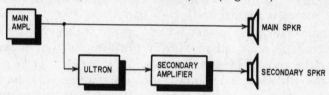

Fig. 118. *Incorporation of the Ultron phase shift unit into an audio system.*

can be shifted by various portions of 360°. For example, if phase is shifted 180°, or half a cycle, this may correspond to the rarefaction portion of a sound wave instead of the compression point

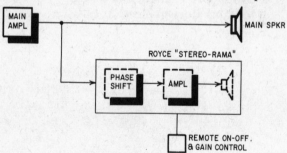

Fig. 119. *Incorporation of the Royce "Stereo-Rama" in an audio system.*

(Fig. 101 on page 12). If phase is delayed a full 360°, then we are back at the beginning point of the cycle. However, the signal has been retarded time-wise by a full cycle. If we can delay a low frequency, say 100 cycles, by a full cycle (which is about 11 feet long) the initial part of the phase-shifted signal will leave the secondary speaker about 11 milliseconds later, since sound travels about 1 foot per millisecond. The ear can appreciate that kind of difference.

One of the commercially available phase-shift units, Holt Stereo, includes not only a phase-shift network but also a complete amplifier, including gain, bass and treble controls. Fig. 117 shows how it is incorporated into the conventional audio system.

According to manufacturer the unit:

"Electronically provides a time delay by a relatively large phase shift over the audio spectrum. The delay in time is different at different frequencies . . . the time delay is smaller at the higher end. We use the same range of time delay as is used in normal hearing to position. The ear does not detect less than 1/15,000 second and the most that is used is a little more than 1/400 second. Because of the distance that the ears are apart, this is the most that is used in normal hearing for positioning what we hear."

A somewhat similar device is the Ultron. Not a complete amplifier, it contains only a phase-shift network intended to be incorporated in the audio system as shown in Fig. 118.

On the other hand, a complete phase-shift ensemble, including phase-shift network, amplifier and speaker all in one housing, is the Stereo-Rama by Royce. Fig. 119 shows how it would be connected to a previously monophonic system. The Stereo-Rama is very much like the Xophonic previously described in that both contain all the equipment required for converting to quasi-stereo. However, the Xophonic changes the signal by acoustic means, while the Stereo-Rama does so electronically.

the stereo effect

B<small>EFORE</small> exploring the mechanics of stereophonic recording, transmission and reproduction, we must come to grips with the subject by asking what it is we are trying to achieve. What kind of sound are we trying to produce? What effects and illusions are we after?

It is much more true of stereo that the listener must be an active participant in the process. It is not sufficient to let the recording and broadcast engineers worry about the theory and techniques of capturing sound in stereo fashion. Although the sound has been successfully recorded on tape or disc or is accurately broadcast by radio, it has to be reproduced in a manner that will achieve the intended effects. Mere possession of stereo equipment will not guarantee satisfying sound. To the extent that the listener is acquainted with the characteristics of stereo, the chances of satisfaction are increased.

Many persons tend to identify the term stereo with directionality —the ability to determine whether the sound source or its individual components are to the right or left, or in front of the listener. While this property can be an important attribute of stereo, it is a mistake to associate stereo exclusively with it.

Stereophonic—to use the full term—derives from the Greek and means solid or full sound. The notion of fullness or solidity goes beyond directionality to include a number of additional factors. Some of them are already well known to us as being the identifying characteristics of good monophonic reproduction, such as wide frequency range, low distortion and high signal-to-noise ratio.

Stereo seeks to go further, enhancing the illusion of reality by bringing us additional qualities associated with the original performance. At the same time, a complete account of the stereo effect must include not only the differences between stereo and mono but also what they have in common. To lose sight of the need for wide frequency response, low distortion, etc. would do injustice to the art of audio reproduction.

Directionality

A great deal of theorizing and experimentation has been devoted to uncovering the factors that enable the mind to place a sound-producing object at a given distance and angle from the listener. While the same factors are mentioned by a number of authorities,

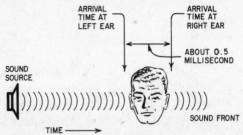

Fig. 201. *Difference in arrival time at each ear of a sound produced by a source to the left of the head.*

there is considerable lack of unanimity as to their relative importance. Thus, one authority attributes spatial location exclusively to one factor and holds that the others merely confirm what the mind already knows. Quite possibly, the relative importance of each factor differs according to the listener, the listening site, the type of sound, and similar circumstances. And there are indications that one factor can substitute for another.

In the main, directionality is attributed by the authorities to differences in (1) time of arrival of sound at each ear; (2) intensity at each ear; (3) phase at each ear; (4) waveform at each ear; (5) the ratio of reverberated to direct sound at each ear.

Arrival-time difference

Sound travels at a rate of nearly 1,100 feet per second at sea level which is slightly more than 1 foot per millisecond. A sound arriving from due left of the listener reaches the left ear before the right, assuming the subject faces straight ahead. Since the space between the ears is from 6 to 8 inches, there is a difference of about

0.5 millisecond in the arrival time (Fig. 201). Apparently the human mind can recognize this difference so as to orient the sound source.

However, if the sound is a pure sine wave, (Fig. 202) and continues for a while, how does the mind distinguish between arrival times? The answer is that it doesn't. Experiments have

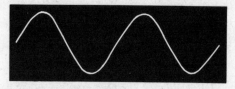

Fig. 202. *A pure sine wave—two cycles.*

been conducted in which subjects were asked to orient a sound source producing a steady pure tone. The lack of accuracy was sufficient to show that such a source did not permit orientation.

A number of authorities believe that this kind of orientation depends upon the transients associated with typical sounds; sel-

Fig. 203. *Typical transient initiating a sound waveform.*

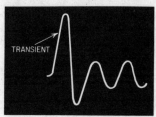

dom is a pure tone found in nature. A transient is a brief burst of energy, and most sounds are initiated by a pulse of one degree or another (Fig. 203). Arrival time concerns the *start* of a sound. Once it has built up to a steady state, the mind can no longer localize it, except by remembering that initially it appeared to come from a given direction. If the sound is built up gradually, without a transient, then the mind may have considerable difficulty in locating the source.

Some interesting experiments have been conducted in which simultaneous photographs were taken of a sound waveform and of the response of the nerves involved in the hearing mechanism. These tests revealed that the nerves discharge a signal to the brain at the first positive peak of the sound.[1] It has been reasoned, therefore, that the mind employs the first positive peak as a reference for measuring time intervals between sounds arriving at each ear;

[1] James Moir, "Stereophonic Reproduction," *Audio*, October, 1952.

but that the process must be frequently repeated to maintain the sense of directionality.

Intensity differences

Differences in the intensity of a given sound at each ear are also considered to be an important factor. Intervention of the head causes a difference in loudness at each ear due to diffraction

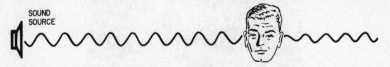

Fig. 204. *Effect of interposition of the head upon amplitude of sound at each ear.*

effect. There is an increase of air pressure on the ear toward the sound and a decrease of pressure on the ear away from it, as illustrated in Fig. 204. The greater the size of the interfering object, the greater the difference between pressures at each ear. And the

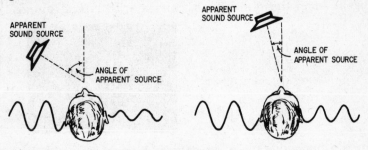

Fig. 205. *Apparent angular location of sound as related to relative loudness at each ear.*

smaller the wavelength—in other words, the higher the frequency —the greater is the pressure difference.

Since the loudness differences are greatest at the high frequencies, the stereo characteristic of directionality is principally associated with the treble range. But there is no agreement as to the lowest frequencies involved. Some place the starting point as low as 250 cycles, and others at 500 or 800 cycles. Some also indicate that frequencies above 7,000 or 8,000 cycles do not contribute to directionality.

Intensity differences are generally considered more important than arrival times for the sensation of directionality. One experimenter has found that a difference in arrival time, stated in milliseconds, has to be five times as great as a difference in intensity at each ear, stated in decibels, to produce the same effect of directionality. This experimenter found that the two effects are interacting and in proper proportions can substitute, reinforce or cancel each other in terms of imparting directionality to sound.

The effectiveness of intensity is indicated by other writers, who state:

"... with sustained tones even a 2-db difference in loudspeaker intensity can produce a shift in the apparent position of the sound source."[2]

Through long experience, the human mind has learned to interpret various levels of loudness at each ear as differences in angular location of a sound source (Fig. 205). Suppose that a sound should seem to come not from the extreme left but about

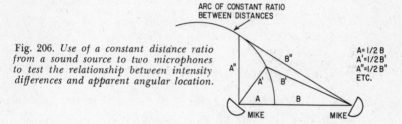

Fig. 206. *Use of a constant distance ratio from a sound source to two microphones to test the relationship between intensity differences and apparent angular location.*

one-third of the way between two speakers spaced along the wall of a room. If the level of the left speaker is higher than that of the right, by the correct amount, the listener will have the illusion that the sound emanates from a point between the speakers and to the left.

To confirm the relationship between relative loudness at each ear and the resulting impression of angular location formed in the mind, the following test was conducted.[3] Using two microphones in fixed position, an arc was drawn (Fig. 206) so that the distances from any point on the arc to each microphone, although unequal, always maintained the same ratio to each other, say 2 to 1. Thus the sound received by the left microphone would always have the same relative loudness compared with the sound picked up by the right microphone if the source were anywhere on the arc. If the right microphone were twice as far away as the left one, then the left microphone would always pick up four times as much (6 db more) sound. A person walked along the arc and spoke at the same time. The sound picked up by each microphone was fed to the

[2] James Cunningham and Robert Oakes Jordan, "Stereophonic Microphone Placement," *Audio*, November, 1956.
[3] W. B. Snow, "Auditory Perspective," *Bell Laboratories Record*, March, 1934.

left and right sides of a pair of earphones worn by participants in the experiment, who could not see the person speaking. They were asked to estimate the speaker's apparent angular location. No matter where the speaker was on the arc, the listeners always tended to ascribe about the same angular location to the sound.

Phase difference

Although a number of references in stereo literature cite phase differences as a factor in directionality, the allusions are generally

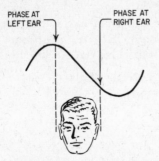

PHASE AT LEFT EAR

PHASE AT RIGHT EAR

Fig. 207. *Typical differences in phase at each ear of a middle-frequency sound.*

vague. Some writers deny that phase plays a role in stereo, at least so far as the directionality effect is concerned.

There is nothing to indicate that the mind has a basis for discerning whether it is the phase at the left ear or the right that corresponds with sound from a given direction. However, the present lack of an explanation does not mean we are certain that phase differences are unimportant.

A sound waveform may be at a different part of the cycle when it reaches one ear than when it reaches the other (Fig. 207). At frequencies below 1,000 cycles, the waveform is long compared to the distance between the ears. Thus, at 500 cycles, a cycle occupies a space of about 2 feet. Hence there will be a considerable difference in the phase of the waveform at each ear. At a high frequency, for example, 5,000 cycles, each cycle is only slightly more than 2 inches and it is possible for the waveform at each ear to be at the same point of the cycle, as shown in Fig. 208. Therefore, phase differences, if they do play a role in stereo, are primarily associated with frequencies below 1,000 cycles.

Waveform difference

Differences in the waveform at each ear are apparently a prime factor in spatial orientation. Most of those who have explored stereophonic phenomena have found that differences in the *nature* of the signal reaching each ear produce a sense of directionality.

The most thorough exposition of this viewpoint is probably that of Hume[4] who goes so far as to hold that waveform differences are *the* factor in directionality, with intensity and arrival-time serving to confirm what the mind already knows.

The head and also the external ear, because of their size and shape, filter the higher frequencies. The head acts as a filter for

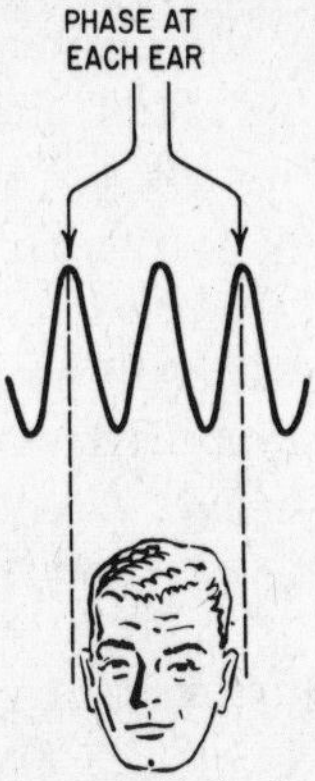

PHASE AT
EACH EAR

Fig. 208. *Possible identity of phase at each ear for high-frequency sounds.*

frequencies above 800 cycles, he states, and the external ear acts as a filter for frequencies above 5,000 cycles.

". . . the stereophonic effect is produced by a difference in high-frequency or harmonic content, created by head and external ear shadowing, of the sound signal reaching the inner ear."

Thus the left ear would receive all the frequencies of a sound arriving from the left, while the sound reaching the right ear would be substantially stripped of its harmonic content, as illustrated in Fig. 209.

Hume conducted the following experiment. An audio oscillator generated a sine wave, which was reproduced by a wide-range amplifier and speaker. The sound was picked up by a microphone, and the microphone output at various frequencies was measured. Next, a block of sound-absorbing material about the size and shape of a human head was placed between the speaker and microphone, and readings were again taken of the microphone output at various frequencies. Then the two sets of readings were compared. At frequencies of 100, 200 and 300 cycles, the readings were 3 db lower when the obstruction was in place. But, with the obstruction in place, the reading was 7 db lower at 1,000 cycles, 8 db lower at 3,000 cycles, 10 db lower at 5,000 cycles, and 7 db lower at 8,000 cycles.

The conclusion was that the high-frequency content of a com-

---

[4] Howard F. Hume, "A New Concept on the Physiological Aspect of Stereophonic Sound," *Audio,* March, 1957.

plex waveform would be considerably smaller on one side of the obstruction than on the other—i.e. at one ear than at the other if the sound arrived from the left or right—so as to alter radically the waveform at the far ear.

The above test was repeated using a square wave instead of a sine wave. When the obstruction was placed between the speaker and the microphone, the output of the microphone, as viewed on an oscilloscope, approached a sine wave, indicating loss of the high-frequency content of the square wave.

Next, two speakers 180° apart, opposite each ear of a listener, were used to reproduce music. Sound was supplied to the speakers through a frequency-discriminating network, one for each speaker, permitting variable high-frequency attenuation with a maximum slope of 4 db per octave. A control permitted the experimenter simultaneously to increase the high-frequency attenuation for one

SOUND SOURCE   COMBINATION OF LOW & HIGH FREQUENCIES   HIGH FREQUENCY FILTERED BY HEAD LEAVING ONLY LOW FREQUENCY

Fig. 209. *Change in waveform due to interposition of the head.*

speaker and decrease it for the other. As this was done the listeners.

"reported an illusion of the artist moving from one side of the stage to the other. . . . The subjects were able to indicate precisely where the artist stood in an arc of 180° in front. Settings of the control were recorded and related to the imagined location of the artist. On repeated tests the subjects maintained a high degree of accuracy in orienting the imagined performer with respect to the control settings. The ear's relative sensitivity to moderately high frequencies—most acute at about 3,000 cycles—helps account for these results obtained by varying the high-frequency content of sounds."

Hume, among others, has suggested that a person with only one good ear or with one ear plugged can identify the sound source "to a surprisingly high degree." Information about the position of the source can be obtained by slight movements of the head, resulting in changes in the waveform at the ear. A person, states Hume, can remember a tone quality—the waveform of a sound—for a certain period of time.

"By moving his head he can compare the wave shapes received at different times, and from these samples decide on the position of the source, even though he is using only one ear to gather the information."

Even though a person with one good ear remains still, nevertheless the head does make slight involuntary movements, resulting in spatial orientation to one extent or another.

He concludes that:

"In the main, left-and-right orientation is provided by head shadowing, while front-and-back orientation [is provided] by external ear shadowing."

Ratio of reverberated to direct sound

In *normal* indoor surroundings, the ears receive sound in two ways (Fig. 210): directly from the source and indirectly as the result of reflections off the walls, ceiling, floor and objects within the room. The ratio of reverberated to direct sound is one factor that permits us to localize the source.

One authority[5] has reported that, when two speakers were used

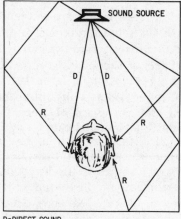

D=DIRECT SOUND
R=REVERBERATED SOUND

Fig. 210. *Illustration of direct and reverberated sound reaching the ears.*

in stereo experiments, the sound appeared to come from the speaker with the smallest ratio; that is, with the relatively smallest proportion of reverberation. He states:

"In general, the localization tends toward the channel giving the most natural or close-up reproduction. . . . Experiment shows that decreasing either the total loudness or the amount of direct sound relative to reverberant gave the impression that the sound was moving back on the stage. Depth localization is thus a complicated function of loudness and relative reverberation."

[5] Snow, *op. cit.*

Considering that in real life one encounters a good deal of reverberation, and since reverberation makes it difficult to distinguish direction, how is it that one can orient sounds? This is attributed to the ability of the mind, particularly through binaural hearing, to distinguish direct sound from the reverberant, possibly on the basis of arrival time, and to give heaviest weight to the direct sound, thereby localizing the source. Binaural discrimination in favor of the direct sound can amount to as much as 10 to 15 db.

In reproduction, the effect of directionality depends, not upon binaural discrimination between direct and reverberated sound, but upon keeping reverberation out of one speaker or the other, so that the source appears to be in the direction of the speaker with the least reverberation.

Spaciousness

One of the most important, perhaps *the* most important, factor in the stereo effect is the sensation of spaciousness. This has nothing to do with assigning direction to the source. Rather, it concerns making the listener feel as though the source itself is large or the performance is taking place in a large hall instead of in the confines of a typical living room. Thus one author has commented:

"The enhanced esthetic appeal obtained from an auditory-perspective reproduction of an orchestra is not due so much to an accurate localization of the various sounds as to a general effect of space distribution, which adds a fullness to the overall effect."[6]

The illusion of spaciousness is produced in several ways. One is by physical distribution of the sound source—if the sound is reproduced by two or more speakers spaced several feet apart this removes the impression that the sound is issuing from a relatively small hole at a particular point in the room. While this may raise certain problems, at least on a theoretical basis, such as partial cancellation at some frequencies or reinforcement at others, due to phase differences when the sound from each speaker meets the ear, most listeners find that reproduction by more than one speaker system adds considerably to enjoyment of music originally produced by a spread source.

A sensation of spaciousness can be obtained by stopping up one ear, which greatly decreases the ability to orient the source of sound and hence fosters the illusion. This is *not* a recommended method of listening but a simple experiment which makes clear one of the phenomena involved in the hearing process. One-eared

---
[6] *Ibid.*

listening, if nothing else, will prove that aural illusions exist; and it is only by means of aural illusions that we can hope to bring a 100-piece orchestra into the average living room.

In great part, the feeling of spaciousness is associated with reverberation. It is estimated that at a musical performance as much as "90% of the sound energy reaching a member of the audience may have been reflected one or more times from the various surfaces in the auditorium."[7] Our ears grow accustomed to associating a certain amount of reverberation—that is, the ratio of reverberated to direct sound and the delay time between the two sounds—with various sizes of halls. When we hear a given amount of reverberation in a confined space, the habits of the mind tend to produce the illusion that we are hearing the sound in a much larger space.

The manner in which the mind associates reflected sound with spaciousness has been described as follows:

"Suppose we are seated in the concert hall and a sound occurs; our ears are struck by the reflections of this sound from all directions, with the direct sound accounting for only a small percentage of the total sound energy reaching the ears. Of course, we localize on the direct sound, but the mind integrates the reflected energy and forms an impression of the size of the hall, perhaps roughly similar to the way in which bats use the reflective radar principle to perceive obstructions."[8]

Reverberation can help impart the illusion of spaciousness in other ways too. Increasing amounts decrease the mind's ability to locate the source. Hence if reverberated sound is produced by the same speaker that produces the original sound, this will decrease the listener's impression that the sound is coming from a specific, small area of the room.

There are limits to everything. An excessive ratio of reverberated to direct sound can become offensive, serving to muddy the sound and otherwise burden the ears. Also, excessive intervals between the arrival time of the direct sound and that of the reverberation can produce an echo rather than a concert-hall effect.

The maximum recommended interval between the original and reverberated sound is 40 to 50 milliseconds. Since sound travels about 1 foot per millisecond, spacing of microphones should be such as not to cause a difference in travel time from the source to each microphone in excess of about 60 feet, as illustrated in Fig. 211. This principle also applies to the distances from the

[7] E. H. Bedell, "Auditorium Acoustics and Control Facilities for Reproductions in Auditory Perspective," *Bell Laboratories Record*, March, 1934.
[8] Cunningham and Jordan, *op. cit.*

stereo speakers to the listener. However, such inequality could occur only in an extremely large room such as a social hall.

Multiplicity effect

Studies of orchestral reproduction indicate that the mind's impression of a large group of violins playing at once depends upon the fact that they are playing not quite together. Slight differences in attack and release time, in pitch and timbre, are responsible for the sound of a *group* of violins. If all the musicians played exactly together, the sound would be that of a single violin greatly amplified.

In a similar fashion, the stereo effect depends to a degree upon multiple sound patterns which differ slightly in some manner —possibly in intensity, phase, waveform or arrival time. One is tempted to draw an analogy. In visual stereo perception two slightly different images simultaneously registered in the mind produce the effect of solidity. While the analogy may not be wholly incorrect, it suffers from the fact that visual stereo depends upon a different image being seen by each eye. In the case of hearing, however, an illusion of solidity can be obtained with just one ear, because of multiple sound patterns. A true analogy would be the three-dimensional illusion that an artist can achieve on a flat surface through skillful use of shading and shadow.

It is understandable therefore why quasi-stereo techniques are effective to varying degrees. Although a single channel serves as the sound source, a feeling of solidity can be imparted by altering the sound's characteristics in some manner as it is reproduced through additional speakers. The sound from each speaker may differ in various ways, in frequency balance, phase, arrival time. And these differences help create the illusion of solidity. Quite possibly, quasi-stereo effects might be obtained from a single speaker.

Dynamic range

Let us consider factors that are the hallmarks of high-quality monophonic reproduction and are essential elements of realistic stereo sound. The order of discussion is of no relevance, and we shall begin with a consideration of dynamic range.

At a live performance by an orchestra, the range between the softest and loudest sounds is between 60 and 70 db. That is, the largest amount of acoustic power generated by the orchestra may be as much as 1,000,000 to 10,000,000 times as great as the smallest.

A large choral group, a brass band and other sources have dynamic ranges of the same order.

Realistic reproduction must permit a substantial part of this range to be re-created. The loudest sounds must not overload the equipment so as to produce noticeable distortion—audible as fuzziness, harshness and breakup. The weakest sounds must be discernible; that is, audible above background noise and that generated by the reproducing equipment.

The usual limitation upon dynamic range is in the electronic

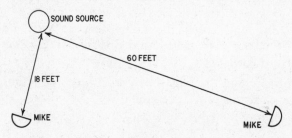

Fig. 211. *Example of echo effect produced by excessive difference in distance between microphones and sound source.*

equipment, due to the noise (including hum) that it produces. When spurious sound is as great as the audio signal, it tends to mask the signal partly or completely. Since many of the sounds associated with the directionality and other characteristics of stereo are of high frequency, and since the high frequencies tend to be the weakest sounds, a limited dynamic range tends to diminish the stereo effect.

A limited dynamic range introduced during recording or radio transmission in itself produces a cramped effect. It is as though the ceiling and floor of a large room were much too close together. If, for example, an original dynamic range of 60 db is confined to 35 db, many of the nuances and accents accomplished by changes in level are limited in their effect; reproduction has taken a step away from realism.

Noise

A high noise level tends to prevent one from hearing the weakest sounds, sounds that may play an important role in the stereo effect. Moreover, noise in itself is an obtrusive factor. In the last analysis, the stereo effect is an illusion which can easily be disrupted by extraneous factors such as hiss, hum, crackles, pops and other forms of noise.

Distortion

Stereo seems to enhance the clarity of musical reproduction and to decrease the apparent distortion. True as this may be, it does not constitute an argument for permitting greater amounts of distortion in stereo than in monophonic reproduction.

The initial impact of stereo upon the listener tends to be so dramatic that differences between poor and excellent speakers, between poor and excellent amplifiers, etc. seem to have little significance. But upon repeated listening, the initial effect tends to wear off and distortion impinges more and more upon the consciousness. It is much the same story as with monophonic equipment, which may have sounded extremely good at first but shows various flaws upon closer acquaintance.

Therefore it may be said that realistic reproduction entails a minimum of distortion. Directionality, spaciousness, etc. cannot compensate for sound which lacks the clarity—the "clean quality" —of the original performance.

Frequency response

As with distortion, some believe that with respect to frequency response less rigorous standards can be applied to stereo than to monophonic reproduction. It is true that a limited frequency range tends to be less noticeable in the case of stereo. But this does not mean that stereo with a range of, say, 50 to 8,000 cycles can be as good as stereo with a range of 50 to 15,000 cycles.

Directionality and other qualities associated with stereo depend in large part upon proper reproduction of the treble range. Transients, associated with directionality, are by their very nature high frequencies. Inadequate reproduction of transients makes itself noticed in loss of directionality and in loss of crispness and cleanness.

Frequency response also pertains to uniformity of response. Acute peaks are likely to be at least as disturbing to the ear in stereo as in monophonic reproduction. In fact, probably more so in stereo, because peaks in one sound channel or the other may cause an apparent shift of source from one speaker to the other.

The importance of wide, smooth frequency response in achieving the stereo effect, namely maximum reality, is indicated by the degree of attention that various experimenters have paid to this factor. Thus the speakers used in the stereo experiments by Bell Laboratories "were designed . . . to respond uniformly over the range from 40 to 15,000 cycles."[9] In stereo experiments conducted by Ampex Corp. special equalizing networks were employed to obtain relatively flat response between 40 and 15,000 cycles from the theater speaker systems employed to re-create the sound of a full orchestra via tape.[10]

Reproduction level

Many individuals are addicted to very high volume levels when using monophonic equipment. In this manner they seek to bring out all the sounds of the original performance, to avoid the apparent loss of bass that occurs at reduced levels (the Fletcher-Munson effect) and to re-create the vibrancy of the original performance. It is common for audiophiles to play music at levels *above* that which one would have heard at the original performance.

It may well be asked whether reproduction levels close to those of the original performance are as important in stereo as in monophonic listening. Before considering this question, let us digress briefly to clarify the meaning of "original level." The reference is not to the acoustic power actually produced by a sound source, for example an orchestra, which may be on the order of hundreds of watts. Rather, the original level refers to the amount of acoustic power that greets the listener's ears at a typical good listening site, say a seat in the 10th or 15th row of a concert hall. In this case, the power involved is in the order of a few watts or even less than 1 watt.

In the main, authorities seem to agree that the stereo illusion is at its fullest when the reproduced music is close to the original level. This does not mean that the reproduced music has to be *fully* as loud as the original. And it does not mean that the music has to be as loud in stereo as in monophonic for equal sensations of reality. What it means, simply, is that by bringing up the volume to a level *approaching* that of the original, one thereby greatly enhances the illusion of reality, of being at a live performance.

This point has been very well expressed by one of the leading manufacturers of speakers:

"It is certainly true that with stereo program material it is no longer necessary to boost the intensity *above* live concert level to hear fine details. But with stereo we feel it even more desirable that material be played at a natural listening level. Most listeners

[9] A. L. Thuras, "Loudspeakers and Microphone for Auditory Perspective," *Bell Laboratories Record*, March, 1934.
[10] Walter T. Selsted and Ross H. Snyder, "Acoustical and Electrical Considerations in Symphony Orchestra Reproduction," *Audio*, January, 1957.

43

seem to feel that as volume is reduced, the 'realistic' quality vanishes even more quickly than with single-channel reproduction. Some stereo recordings of symphonic works sound very much like single-channel material until they are played *very* loud, and then suddenly the whole orchestra opens up and the effect is magnificent."[11]

---

[11] Correspondence from James B. Lansing Sound, Inc.

stereo on the air

STEREO broadcasting—or stereocasting—can be divided into four categories: (1) FM–AM, which uses a frequency-modulation station to transmit one channel of a stereo program and an amplitude-modulation station to transmit the second; this is frequently called simulcasting. (2) FM–FM, in which two FM stations broadcast the two stereo signals (frequently called multicasting). (3) Multiplexing, whereby both channels of the stereo program are transmitted by a single FM station, employing recently perfected techniques. Multiplex is the logical vehicle for stereocasting. (4) AM stereo in which both channels are transmitted by one AM station.

There are two multiplex techniques, known as the Halstead and the Crosby systems, which will be explained presently.

Simulcasting

FM–AM has been most popular method of stereocasting to date. Its basic elements are shown in Fig. 301. As of late 1958, simulcasts were taking place in over 50 cities for periods ranging from as little as 1/2 hour to as much as 20 hours or more per week. In addition, several areas were broadcasting stereo by means of an AM and a TV station.

Although FM–AM stereocasting has definite technical limitations with respect to the other stereo methods, it's relative popularity is due to the fact that it makes the least demands on both the broadcaster and the listener in terms of equipment. A substantial number of AM stations have FM adjuncts, so relatively little is required in the way of additional facilities to broadcast the channel L and channel R portions of the stereo program over separate transmitters. On the listener's part, he need not have a complete second high-fidelity system to reproduce the second channel. As Fig. 302 shows, instead of a complete chain of high-fidelity components, he may merely substitute an AM radio. True, this will not duplicate the audio quality of a high-fidelity system, but it enables the listener to bring stereo into his home, if only on a temporary basis until he obtains better equipment for the second channel.

In catering to stereo listeners, the FM–AM broadcaster must not overlook his far larger (as yet) monophonic audience. He must see to it that each of the stereo microphones picks up substantially all the sound so that neither the monophonic listener on FM nor the one on AM is deprived of a significant part of the program material. In other words, the distance between the channel L and channel R microphones must not be exaggerated for stereo effect at the cost of inadequate monophonic reproduction. On the other hand, to bring the microphones too close together might tend to reduce the stereo effect. Thus the FM–AM broadcaster must follow a course of compromise.

To use the words of the chief engineer of WQXR in New York City, one of the early stereocasters:

"Any broadcaster . . . under the present system needs to use utmost caution in microphone placement so as not to degrade either channel for the monaural [monophonic] listener. As we have control over our live pickups, you'll find our spacing to be moderate (actually the stereo effect can be had with a very minimum of spacing) and rarely do we exceed a spacing of 4 feet. It should be kept in mind that our musical groups are in the chamber-music classification, quartet, quintet, two-piano, etc."[1]

On the other hand, the FM–AM stereocaster faces a difficult problem when placement of microphones is out of his control, which is the case when he broadcasts a commercial stereo tape or disc. He must avoid material recorded with widely spaced microphones, unless he is willing to let monophonic transmission suffer. The fact that simulcasting is thus limited as to its program material is one of the factors pointing to the desirability of multiplex (the Crosby system) as the way to transmit stereo.

Another major difficulty in FM–AM stereocasting is the fact that the AM signal is subject to considerable degradation. This

---

[1] Correspondence from Mr. Louis J. Kleinklaus, Station WQXR, New York City, N.Y.

may occur at the transmitter, in the air or at the receiving end. One respect in which the AM signal suffers is frequency response; that is, response at the high end. While it is true that a number

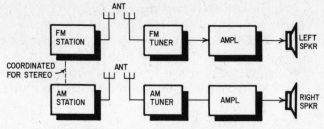

Fig. 301. *FM-AM stereo—"Simulcasting."*

of AM stations broadcast a signal flat to 10,000 to 12,000 cycles, and occasionally to 15,000 cycles, all of which fall within the limits of high fidelity, on the other hand many AM stations find it necessary to cut response sharply above 5,000 cycles to avoid

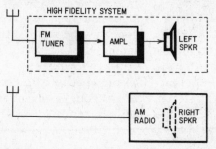

Fig. 302. *Adding stereo at minimum cost.*

interference with stations on nearby frequencies. The wider the audio range transmitted by the station, the greater are the possibilities of interference.

Even when the transmitted signal extends to 10,000 cycles or better, few AM tuners are capable of preserving this frequency response. Many, even those labeled high fidelity, provide flat response to only 5,000 or 6,000 cycles. Several exceptional ones maintain response to about 8,000 or 9,000 cycles.

On the other hand, if FM–AM broadcasting survives as a medium for stereo, there are indications that the problem of full-range frequency response on the AM channel may be overcome by a relatively new broadcasting technique, single sideband transmission (SSB). So far as commercial broadcasting is concerned, SSB is still in the experimental stage. It enables a station to broadcast

47

twice as great a frequency range as at present, within the same portion of the radio-frequency spectrum.

For the time being, however, the AM channel is definitely limited as to high-frequency response—in transmission or reception or both. Attenuation of high frequencies in one of the channels impairs the stereo illusion and tends to focus the ears excessively upon the speaker with the greatest high-frequency content.

The AM method of propagating a radio wave suffers by comparison with FM in that it is much more subject to noise, fading

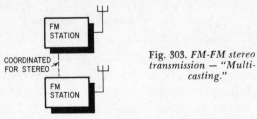

Fig. 303. *FM-FM stereo transmission — "Multicasting."*

and other troubles. In a strong-signal area, relatively close to the transmitting antenna, the signal may be sufficiently noise-free to be considered suitable for high-fidelity reception. Unfortunately, a great many listeners are at distances which cause the defects of AM to become apparent. The presence of appreciable noise and other types of interference in just one speaker, as the result of using AM for one of the channels, tends to disrupt the illusion of a sound source spread across the room.

Multicasting

As illustrated in Fig. 303, multicasting is basically the same as simulcasting, except that the second channel is transmitted by an FM station instead of the AM adjunct of an FM station. Hence it is often necessary to obtain cooperation between two independent stations, not always easy in a competitive world. On the receiving end, considerably fewer listeners are likely to have an extra FM tuner and associated reproducing equipment as compared with those having an AM receiver in addition to an FM tuner. Hence FM–FM stereocasting has made very little progress, and present indications are that it will play a limited role in the future.

On the other hand, the demand for FM–FM stereocasting has made itself felt to the extent that several stations have undertaken this form of broadcasting, and listeners have managed to get around the problem of an extra FM tuner. According to the program director of WBUR in Boston, which cooperates with WGBH in the same city to transmit FM–FM stereo programs:

"... AM–FM stereo had been available through a commercial station in Boston, but what people seem to appreciate most was the opportunity to hear all-FM stereo. We have received many letters which indicate that listeners pool their equipment in order to receive broadcasts."[2]

From the technical point of view, FM–FM can provide extremely good results, the task of coordinating two independent FM stations presenting no especially difficult problems. However, it suffers from the same limitation as FM–AM in that wide microphone spacing cannot be used if each station is also to serve its monophonic listeners adequately.

There is a further problem, though probably a slight one, on the receiving end if two FM tuners of different make are used. As shown in Fig. 304, the FM station supplies a certain amount

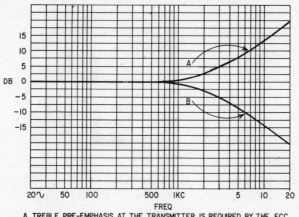

A. TREBLE PRE-EMPHASIS AT THE TRANSMITTER IS REQUIRED BY THE FCC
B. TREBLE DE-EMPHASIS IS NEEDED AT THE TUNER TO PRODUCE FLAT RESPONSE

Fig. 304. *Treble pre-emphasis and de-emphasis in FM transmission and reception.*

of pre-emphasis of the treble frequencies, and the tuner must supply a corresponding amount of treble de-emphasis to achieve flat response. At the same time, de-emphasis reduces noise, which is the reason for this scheme of things. Unfortunately, not all tuners incorporate the standard amount of de-emphasis shown in Fig. 304. Some provide less than the required treble cut, so that the net result is treble boost, causing the output of the tuner to be on the brilliant side. Using two tuners with different de-emphasis curves, the result will be a different relative quantity of treble in each speaker, with resulting detriment to the stereo

[2] Correspondence from Mr. Roderick D. Rightmire, Station WBUR, Boston, Mass.

illusion (unless, by chance, the signal from the more brilliant tuner is fed to the duller of two speakers).

In connection with FM–FM broadcasting (and FM–AM as well) it is interesting to note that some listeners have had the opportunity of hearing three-channel stereo, using TV as a third channel. Stations WGBH and WBUR in Boston have cooperated on a program of this type, transmitting the left and right channels, while a TV pickup was independently set up to provide the sound of the center channel.

Multiplexing

Although progress has been slowest in multiplexing, nevertheless this technique of stereocasting holds the greatest promise for the future, at least from a technical standpoint. It permits a stereo program to emanate from a single station, to maintain high quality on both channels and to give both the stereo and monophonic listener maximum benefits. By attaching a special multiplex

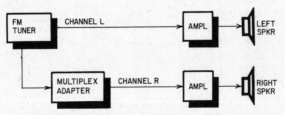

Fig. 305. *Elements of a multiplex receiving system.*

adapter to his present FM tuner, the listener in an FM area will be able to obtain a second sound channel from a given FM station (Fig. 305). Channel L sound is supplied by the FM tuner to an amplifier and speaker in conventional manner. The adapter takes a signal from an appropriate point inside the tuner and from this signal derives the channel R sound, which is fed to a second amplifier–speaker chain.

Historical background

FM multiplexing is linked with the name of Maj. Edwin H. Armstrong, who pioneered the FM technique of radio transmission, making possible noise-free, low-distortion, wide-frequency radio reception. In 1934, 1939–40 and after World War II, he conducted experiments that led to the concepts reflected in today's multiplex equipment. Following World War II, a number of companies and research laboratories became interested in the problem of using a radio station to broadcast not only sound but also facsimile signals, which permit photographs, printed information, etc. to be transmitted through the air. One problem was to avoid having the facsimile signal interfere with the audio signal and thereby impair the quality of the latter. Eventual solution of the problem of simultaneous facsimile and audio transmission pointed the way to broadcasting two audio signals without mutual interference and with satisfactorily low noise and distortion.

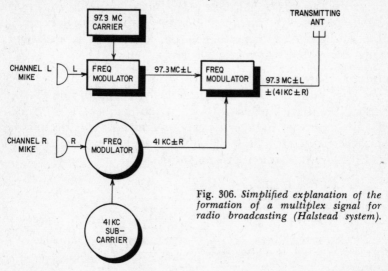

Fig. 306. *Simplified explanation of the formation of a multiplex signal for radio broadcasting (Halstead system).*

The first public demonstration of multiplex transmission was conducted by Multiplex Development Corp. in 1950 in New York City, with two spaced microphones being used to pick up an instrumental trio at experimental station KE2XKH. At that time, the frequency response of the second channel, called the sub-channel, was limited to 8,000 cycles. Even so, the demonstration was impressive.

Armstrong and his research group at Columbia University demonstrated their multiplex system in 1953. However, the system was not compatible in that it did not permit the monophonic listener to continue using his existing tuner. A special tuner had to be purchased to receive a program transmitted by the Armstrong multiplex technique, even though the listener was interested only in monophonic reception. On the other hand, the methods developed by other groups permitted the owner of a conventional FM tuner to continue its use, regardless whether a multiplex program was transmitted by the station to which he was tuned.

By 1955, multiplex was ready for public use. Equipment had been developed capable of satisfying high-fidelity requirements with respect to frequency response, distortion and signal-to-noise ratio. This equipment enabled response out to 15,000 cycles to be obtained on the subchannel as well as on the main channel. The signal-to-noise ratio was better than 60 db on the main channel and at least 55 db on the subchannel, which compares with monophonic FM and is better than the signal-to-noise ratio ordinarily obtained on AM. Distortion, both harmonic and inter-modulation, was kept below 0.5% on the main channel and 1.5% on the subchannel at maximum signal level (full modulation), meeting high-fidelity standards.

Multiplex transmission and reception

Figs. 306 and 307, depicting the Halstead multiplex system, furnish elementary but basic explanations of how a multiplex signal is formed for broadcast purposes and how it is deciphered at the receiving end. In Fig. 306, the rectangles represent channel L and the circles channel R. The audio signal of channel L, or L

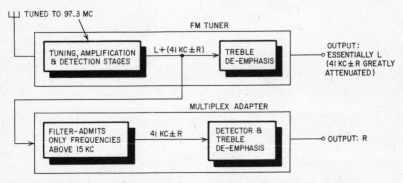

Fig. 307. *Simplified explanation of the detection of the L and R components of a multiplex signal.*

for short, is combined with a radio frequency, called the carrier. For illustrative purposes we will assume that the carrier frequency is 97.3 megacycles. The combination of L and the 97.3 carrier takes place in a frequency modulator. The result is that the carrier varies above and below its original frequency in accordance with the amplitude of L, and the number of such variations per second depends upon the frequency of L. This is frequency modulation, and we may represent it by the expression 97.3-mc $\pm$ L.

Similarly the channel R audio signal, which we call R for short, frequency-modulates another carrier. This time, the carrier instead of being in megacycles is just a little above the audio range. A carrier frequency for stereo might be 41 kilocycles. The result of modulating 41 kc in accordance with the multiplex amplitude of R may be written as 41-kc $\pm$ R.

Then the 41-kc $\pm$ R signal combines with the 97.3-mc $\pm$ L signal in a third frequency modulator. The final result is 97.3 mc $\pm$ L $\pm$ (41 kc $\pm$ R). In other words, the radio carrier frequency is modulated both by L and by 41 kc, with the latter in turn modulated by R. This is what goes on the air.

In Fig. 307 we see how the process is reversed. First the multiplex signal is brought in by a conventional FM tuner, which is dialed to 97.3 mc. The conventional tuner detects both the L and the 41-kc $\pm$ R signals. These are fed to the treble de-emphasis circuit since the FM signal must undergo treble attenuation to compensate for treble boost at the broadcast station. At the output of the conventional tuner, therefore, we have a flat L signal and a greatly attenuated 41-kc $\pm$ R signal. Since the latter is above the audio range, it cannot be heard in any case.

Going back to the point in the tuner where the L and 41-kc $\pm$ R

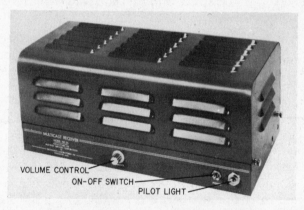

VOLUME CONTROL
ON-OFF SWITCH
PILOT LIGHT

Fig. 308. *Single-frequency multicast receiver.*
(Courtesy Multiplex Corp.)

signals have been detected but not yet de-emphasized, these signals are fed to the multiplex adapter. The adapter admits only signals above 15,000 cycles. Having admitted the 41-kc $\pm$ R signal and eliminated the L signal, the adapter proceeds to detect the R audio information. Thus, the adapter provides an R signal at its output.

Progress to date

A multiplex installation in an existing FM station is not merely a question of adding equipment to provide a second channel, but of integrating the new apparatus with the old. Often the old equipment has not been designed to meet the rigorous performance standards required for satisfactory multiplex service. Hence, in converting an FM station to multiplex substantial changes usually have to be made in the existing apparatus at the same time that the new elements are added.

The purchaser of background music rents a special tuner, such as the one shown in Fig. 308, which is tuned to a single frequency —that of the station selling background music on the second channel. This unit consists of a more or less conventional FM tuner and an adapter. It also includes an audio amplifier capable of driving several speakers at normal background-music level. Included in the adapter is a muting device that, at the will of the station, can shut off the sound; this is achieved by means of special control signals broadcast by the station and tuned in by the multiplex unit. The purpose of the muting device is to turn off portions of the program, such as news, time, etc., intended for some customers and not for others. The unit shown in Fig. 308 also contains a volume control, on–off switch and bass and treble controls. (These latter two controls are not shown in the photo.)

Although multiplex is now used essentially for selling music and other program material on the subchannel, the technical and practical development of this medium may be considered a prelude to its use for the home. With the growing interest in stereo and the demand for stereo program material, in large part due to the role played by stereo discs and tapes, there will be an increasing number of factors working toward the adoption of multiplex for stereo service. Employing the subchannel for public broadcasts will not necessarily work financial hardship on the broadcaster. For one thing, multiplex might be made available on a subscription basis. For another, it is possible for an FM multiplex station to broadcast not only one but two subchannels, one of which could be devoted to public use (it is public service that entitles a broadcast station to its license) and the other to serving commercial customers, such as restaurants, etc., who pay for their music.

Subscription multiplex

Because of the cost of setting up for multiplex transmission, it has been suggested that the subchannel be made available to the public on a subscription basis. Such a proposal has been made by Multiplex Services Corp.

Fig. 309 is a picture of a possible Multicast adapter which

could be attached by the home listener to his FM tuner. The tuner would need an output jack intended for multiplex use; this jack is connected to the audio signal prior to treble de-emphasis. At the bottom of the adapter there are five pushbuttons: "main-channel program," "stereophonic program," "subchannel music

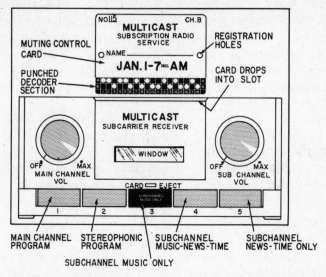

Fig. 309. *Multiplex adapter proposed by Multiplex Services Corp.*

only," "subchannel music–news–time" and "subchannel news–time only." To hear the program normally obtainable with a conventional tuner, the listener would push button 1. For a special program without commercial announcements, available only on the subchannel, he would push button 3. If there were a stereo program on the air and he wished to avail himself of it, he would push button 2, so that both main channel and subchannel would be simultaneously put to use. For the news and time as well as the special program material available on the subchannel, he would push button 4. And he would depress button 5 if he were interested purely in news and time checks; the adapter would be silenced the rest of the time by control signals transmitted by the station.

The special adapter (Fig. 309) would be operated by the control card also shown in that figure. The card would cover the period of a week and would be sold to the listener on an annual, monthly or other basis. To permit the adapter to operate, the control card purchased by the subscriber would have to be inserted. This card would contain punched holes allowing the adapter to work correctly.

To prevent unauthorized use of program material transmitted on the subchannel, the station would send out an "interference" signal on the subchannel. This could take the form of an annoying sound, such as a squeal or howl. The purpose of the control card sold to the subscriber would be to remove the annoying interference signal. The transmitter would send out on the subchannel a series of code pulses at superaudible frequencies. The control card would cause the adapter to make contacts enabling it to receive these code pulses. The code and the corresponding punched holes in the card would be varied each week.

Behind the subscription plan is the thought that the revenue would enable FM stations to provide the best in stereo, featuring top-quality tapes, discs and live programs. The costs of broadcasting a live symphony concert are not small, and a subscription plan for stereo broadcasts could make it economically possible to bring the audiophile closer to the ideal of completely realistic reproduction.

Matrixing—Crosby multiplex system

In FM–AM stereo broadcasting, to preserve the quality of signal on each station, it is necessary to avoid spacing the microphones

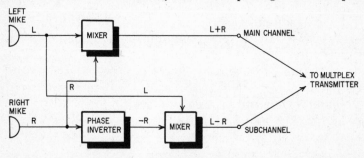

Fig. 310. *"Matrixing" the stereo signals for a multiplex broadcast (Crosby system).*

too far apart lest one or both fail to pick up an appreciable portion of the sound. This criticism also applies to FM–FM stereo and the Halstead system. In other words, if appropriate microphone spacing is used for a multiplex stereo broadcast, the person listening on monophonic equipment (main channel only) may receive only a portion of the music. The Crosby system solves this problem as indicated in Fig. 310.

The audio signals of channels L and R, as picked up by the respective microphones, are added to produce a composite signal, L + R, which contains all the sound. This L + R signal is broadcast on the main channel. Then one of the signals, say the R signal, is subjected to a phase inversion of 180°. That is, at a given moment when the original R signal is positive, the phase-inverted signal will be negative, etc. The phase-inverted signal is called —R. When —R is added to the L signal, their sum is L — R. In other words we have the difference between the two signals (difference signal) which is broadcast on the subchannel.

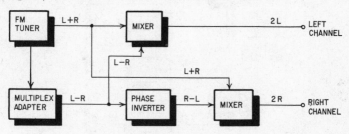

Fig. 311. *Matrixing network for combining the L + R and L — R signals to obtain separate left and right audio signals (Crosby system).*

At the receiving end, the listener would obtain the L + R signal on his conventional FM tuner; he would receive all the program material even though the microphones had been spaced a considerable distance apart. The multiplex adapter would yield the L — R signal for stereo purposes. Then a special "matrixing"—or combining—circuit would function, as shown in Fig. 311: (1) The L + R and L — R signals would be added to produce a 2L signal. (2) The L — R signal would be inverted 180° to produce R — L. Then R — L would be added to L + R, resulting in a 2R signal.

Thus the matrixing network would achieve separation of the L and R signals, each of them available at the output of the multiplex adapter.

In addition to presenting the monophonic listener with the total audio signal, the Crosby system, it is claimed, solves another problem—transmitting a second subchannel for commercial purposes (sale of background music, etc.) without significantly degrading the quality of the first subchannel for stereo purposes. When two subchannels are transmitted (in addition to the main channel), frequency response on each is limited to about 8,000 cycles. Under the Halstead system, the main stereo channel would have a response to 15,000 cycles, while the subchannel would have a response only to 8,000 cycles. The resulting difference in quality between the sounds emanating from the left and right speakers, it is claimed, would be deleterious to the stereo effect.

Under the Crosby system, however, it would not be the L or R signal that is limited in frequency response. The limitation would be of the L—R signal, transmitted on the subchannel, and therefore the sound from the left and right speakers would be equally

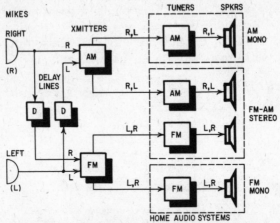

Fig. 312. *Becker method of FM–AM stereo broadcasting.*
(Also suitable for FM–FM and Halstead FM multiplex).

affected. A symmetrical loss in quality, it is held, is much less likely to be noticed. Moreover, the nature of the loss is such that at frequencies above 8,000 cycles both speakers produce virtually the same sound. As will be recalled from the discussion in Chapter 2, several authorities believe that frequencies above 8,000 cycles contribute little if anything to the stereo effect. Hence, it does not matter if there is no stereo separation above 8,000 cycles, according to the proponents of the Crosby approach.

The Becker method

In contrast to the Crosby solution to the problem of supplying the total sound to the monophonic listener despite wide microphone spacing, another approach has been proposed that is applicable to stereo broadcasts by means of the Halstead multiplex system, FM–AM or FM–FM. The method is shown in Fig. 312 in relation to FM–AM stereo broadcasting, as proposed by the inventor.[3]

Microphone L supplies an L signal to the FM transmitter, while microphone R supplies an R signal to the AM transmitter. The

---

[3] Floyd K. Becker, Patent No. 2,819,342, assigned to Bell Telephone Labs, Inc.

L signal is also fed to the AM transmitter through a delay line, which causes the stereo listener to hear signal L from the right speaker several milliseconds after he hears it from the left one. However, according to the inventor, when two identical sounds are heard in quick succession, the earlier one determines its apparent direction. Therefore, the listener would attribute the L signal to a source from the left even though it issues from both speakers. Similarly, the R signal is fed to the AM transmitter through a delay line, which causes the stereo listener to hear it from the left speaker a few milliseconds after he has heard it from the right speaker, so that the apparent direction of the R signal is from the right.

Now consider the monophonic listener. If he is listening to FM, he hears the signals picked up by both the L and R microphones, although the R signal undergoes a slight delay, which the inventor holds to be negligible. If he is listening to AM, he similarly receives both signals, with one slightly but negligibly delayed.

The method of Fig. 312 could be applied to the Halstead multi-

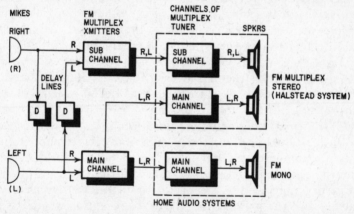

Fig. 313. *Application of the Becker method to FM multiplex stereo under the Halstead system.*

plex technique, as shown in Fig. 313. The L microphone feeds the main channel of the multiplex transmitter, while the R microphone feeds the subchannel. The R signal is fed through a delay line to the main channel, enabling the monophonic (main-channel) listener to hear all the sound. And, for symmetry of sound from both speakers, the L signal can be fed through a delay line to the subchannel.

The Becker method raises the question of reverberation effect due to the production of the same sound by two speakers at slightly different times. Optimum delay time, according to the inventor, is in the region of 5 to 30 milliseconds. A delay approaching 30 milliseconds might result in substantial reverberation effect, which is not unnecessarily unpleasant if the music is acoustically "dry" (lacking reverberation). However, a time delay closer to 5 milliseconds might reduce the added reverberation to negligible proportions, yet permit the Becker method to operate effectively.

Stereo AM

Late in 1958, RCA announced the development of an all-AM stereo technique, employing but one AM broadcast station and one AM tuner. At the time, the new technique—still in the experimental stage—was regarded as being far from ready for commercial application.

The signal broadcast by an AM station consists of the carrier frequency (550–1,600 kc) accompanied by nearby frequencies resulting from audio modulation of the carrier. These adjacent frequencies, called sidebands, fall equally above and below the carrier frequency in the case of conventional AM broadcasts; each sideband is a mirror image of the other.

However, for stereo, a special transmitter is used that permits one sideband to represent the left channel and the other sideband the right channel. A special tuner separates the two sidebands and extracts from each the left or right signal. Stereo AM is compatible in the sense that a conventional AM tuner will receive and detect either sideband, providing the listener with the total audio information in monophonic fashion.

While stereo AM can offer superior performance compared with monophonic AM, on the other hand it would still suffer from the present defects of AM compared with FM—limited frequency range, noise, susceptibility to interference from other stations and the greater irregularity of reception (fading, etc.).

Early in 1959 another AM stereo system was proposed by Philco Corp. This method would use a combination of amplitude and phase modulation (which is akin to frequency modulation). Also, it would use the sum-and-difference frequency principle. The L + R signal would be transmitted by conventional amplitude modulation. Hence the system would be compatible for existing AM receivers would thereby detect the full audio information. The L − R signal would be transmitted by means of phase modulation. A special receiver would detect the L + R and the L − R signals and then combine them in the manner required to obtain separate L and R signals.

Other stereo systems

Stereo, as we have it on records, is an accomplished fact. Stereo broadcasting, on the other hand, is the fastest-moving subject in the stereo picture. Even while this book was being set in type a number of new systems were proposed. These are in addition to the RCA AM-only technique and Philco's proposed combination of phase and amplitude modulation on AM stations.

Motorola Inc. and station WGN-TV, Chicago, jointly presented a demonstration of a proposed stereophonic TV system, using present TV standards but adding a multiplex sound subcarrier.

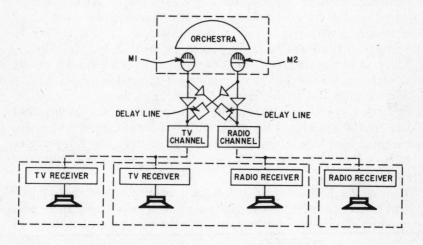

Fig. 314. *Bell Telephone stereophonic system.*

The compatible stereo—mono system has a matrixing stage to direct sounds to the proper audio-amplification channels. The subcarrier bandwidth is 5 kilocycles.

Calbest Electronics Co., Los Angeles, announced the development of a compatible stereo FM system which uses a "narrow-band" multiplex subcarrier, making possible two subcarriers, in addition to the main carrier, on a single FM channel (the second for such subsidiary uses as monophonic music beamed to stores and factories). The Calbest technique employs a sum-and-difference method, with a crossover at 3,500 cycles, the output of both channels being identical at frequencies above this point.

AM stereophony by two methods was proposed almost simultaneously by Bell Telephone and Westinghouse. The Bell system was for two-station transmission (one channel through the television receiver, the other through the AM or FM receiver, for example). The Westinghouse is a multiplex system, with both channels transmitted on the same AM frequency. It can be received with two ordinary broadcast receivers. Both are fully compatible with monophonic reception.

In the Westinghouse system, based on a 30-year-old patent by Dr. Frank Conrad, the broadcast-band carrier is amplitude-modulated with the sum of the right and left channels and frequency-modulated with their difference. A narrow band is used and stereophonic information is transmitted in the band from 300 to 3,000 cycles.

At the receiver, the AM and FM signals are detected and ma-trixed to give the L and R outputs. Reasonably good quality can be attained with two ordinary AM broadcast receivers. One is tuned slightly above, the other slightly below the signal frequency. The AM in the two receivers is identical, but the receivers tuned to each side of the FM transmission act somewhat like a Travis discriminator, with the result that the FM audio signal is in opposite phase in each. Thus one receiver may be said to be pick-ing up AM + FM and the other, AM − FM. Since the AM is the sum and the FM is the difference of the two channels, this resolves to L + R + (L − R) and L + R − (L − R), or left and right channels.

Since the Bell system depends on transmission by an AM and an FM station, or radio and TV station, it is not multiplex and doesn't require FCC authorization. It feeds the signal from both microphones to each channel, but the signal from the right channel is delayed about 10 milliseconds before being fed to the left, and vice versa. With only one receiver, the two channels blend into perfect monophonic reception; with two, the ear locates the sound as coming from the speaker from which it is heard first (appar-ently an old trick, the ear has learned to distinguish the source of sound from echoes and reverberations). In practice, a true stereo effect is obtained.

Still another technique, known as the Percival Stereo radio sys-tem, has been proposed. In this system only one compatible audio signal is transmitted but, in addition, the information as to direc-tion is transmitted in a bandwidth of 100 cps on a subcarrier at a much lower effective power than the audio information. The operation of the system depends on the separation of the direc-tional information from two normal left and right stereo signals in an encoder, the combination of the left and right signals to form a single audio signal, and the reinsertion of the directional information at the receiver by a decoder.

stereo on discs

B ECAUSE of convenience, relatively low cost, and popularity of the phonograph record as a medium for audio reproduction, stereo on a wide scale awaited the development of the stereo disc. First announced to the public in 1957, stereo discs, together with the required reproducing equipment, became available in 1958, a remarkably short interval between promise and fulfillment.

While a variety of methods have been proved or claimed to be suitable for inscribing two audio channels on a phonograph record, the RIAA (Record Industry Association of America) has chosen as the standard the system developed by Westrex Corp., also known as the 45/45 system. As shown in Fig. 401, a record groove is shaped like a V. One wall of the groove, when it bears stereo information, contains the audio signal for the left channel, while the other wall contains the signal for the right channel. Each wall is at an angle of 45° to horizontal and since the stereo information is inscribed on the walls, the term 45/45 has been applied to this system.

Selection of the Westrex system was not necessarily predicated upon its being the best of all possible methods. However, at the time this system was adopted it had proved itself to be practical and was as good as any then available. Therefore it was the logical choice for satisfying the demand for stereo on phonograph records. It would have been impractical, wasteful and confusing for each recording company to decide for itself what system to use. The situation would have been much worse than the period prior to

1954, when various companies were using different equalization characteristics, so that one was confronted with the problem of obtaining equipment that could equalize any of a dozen or more characteristics.

But stereo is still very much in its formative years, and it would be unwise to dismiss methods other than the Westrex as merely of historical or academic interest. Some of the other systems incorporate principles of definite value. In the history of the electronic art, many an advance has been achieved by reverting to an old but basic idea. To the extent that there is merit in the other systems, it is quite possible that future developments will borrow from them and the Westrex might be superseded. To cite paral-

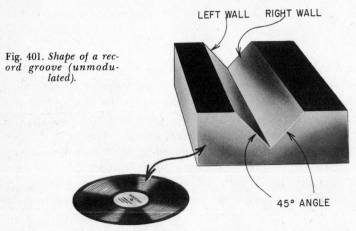

LEFT WALL   RIGHT WALL

Fig. 401. *Shape of a record groove (unmodulated).*

45° ANGLE

lels, 78-rpm records were replaced by 33-1/3- and 45-rpm discs for high-quality reproduction, and FM was proven a more superior method of radio broadcasting than AM.

For the sake of perspective, let us classify the various methods of putting stereo information into a record groove:

1. *Dual-groove records:* Two grooves are recorded, one for the left and the other for the right channel. One method uses the outer diameter of the record to record one channel and the inner for the other. Another technique would record the two grooves on opposite sides of the disc. In each case, dual and properly coordinated playback cartridges are required.

2. *Single-groove records, two-dimensional:* The information for both channels is recorded in one groove, which causes the stylus of the playback cartridge to move in two dimensions; that is,

vertically as well as laterally. The vertical–lateral techniques are embodied in the British (EMI, Sugden and London), Westrex and CBS (Columbia Broadcasting System) Laboratories systems.

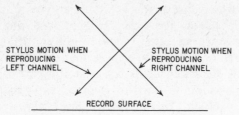

STYLUS MOTION WHEN REPRODUCING LEFT CHANNEL

STYLUS MOTION WHEN REPRODUCING RIGHT CHANNEL

RECORD SURFACE

Fig. 402. *Direction of stylus motion when reproducing either channel of a Westrex stereo groove.*

3. *Single-groove records, one-dimensional:* In this case the groove causes the playback stylus to move only laterally, as in the case of a monophonic recording. A carrier frequency is employed as the vehicle for the second channel. The Minter stereo disc, for one, employs this principle.

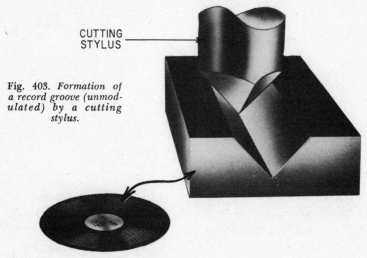

CUTTING STYLUS

Fig. 403. *Formation of a record groove (unmodulated) by a cutting stylus.*

Historical background

EMI in England was experimenting with a stereo disc as far back as 1931, and a patent on a vertical–lateral system was granted to one of its engineers in 1933. In the same year attention was called to the possibilities of a 45/45 system. Also in the early 1930's, Bell Laboratories conducted experiments along the same vein, and two of their engineers were granted a patent in 1938 after having succeeded in making a stereo disc in 1936. The advent of World War II deferred research into stereo discs until after 1945.

The first stereo disc made available to the public was that of Emory Cook (Cook Records). It employed dual grooves, one inscribed toward the outer edge of the record and the other toward the center. This disc appeared in 1952. In the meantime, in England, EMI renewed its research and two other companies, Sugden and London (known in England as Decca) became interested in the problem. In the United States, Westrex Corp., then an affiliate of Bell Telephone Laboratories, began its research. In 1957, Sugden, London and Westrex announced and demonstrated working systems. Sugden's and London's were vertical–lateral techniques. Motion of the stylus in a direction horizontal to the record surface caused one channel to be reproduced; stylus motion in a vertical direction reproduced the other channel. The Westrex

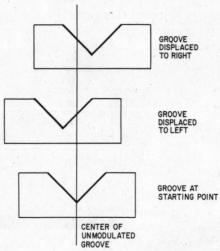

Fig. 404. *Cross-sections of a laterally modulated groove.*

system, so to speak, gave the vertical–lateral technique a 45° twist, with motion of the stylus at a 45° angle to the record in one direction causing one channel to be reproduced, and in the other direction the second channel (Fig. 402).

How the Westrex system works

As a basis for understanding the Westrex method of inscribing and of playing back a record groove, let us review the nature of a monophonic groove and of the movement of the cutting and the playback stylus in it. The groove is cut by a wedge-shaped stylus (Fig. 403), which literally plows a path through the record material. As drawn in Fig. 403, the path is a straight one, which means that no audio signal is being recorded.

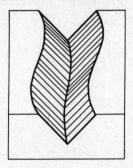

Fig. 405. *A laterally modulated record groove.*

When a signal is applied to the mechanism that drives the cutting stylus, it moves from side to side in accordance with the signal. Fig. 404 shows a cross-section of the record groove and

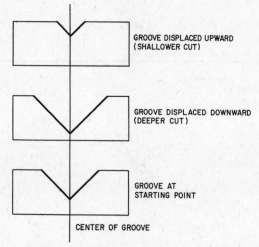

Fig. 406. *Cross-sections of a vertically modulated groove.*

how the stylus moves to the left and right about the central starting point as it responds to the signal. Fig. 405 is a three-dimensional view of the groove after it has been cut by a laterally moving stylus. Figs. 404 and 405 make clear that a playback stylus resting in such a groove will move laterally in corresponding fashion, causing the cartridge's transducing element, (which converts

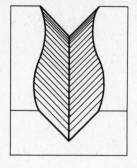

Fig. 407. *A vertically modulated record groove.*

mechanical motion into an electrical signal) to produce a voltage corresponding to the undulations of the groove. The member to

Fig. 408. *Cross-sections of a 45° record groove containing only left channel modulation.*

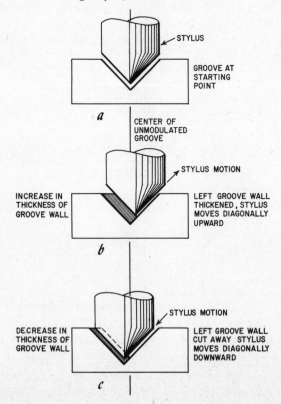

which the stylus is attached will either exert pressure upon a piezoelectric element or will cut through a magnetic field, thereby generating a voltage.

In the past, grooves have been recorded vertically, causing the

Fig. 409. *A stereo groove containing only left-channel modulation.*

Fig. 410. *A stereo groove containing only right-channel modulation.*

playback stylus to move up and down and in this manner develop a signal voltage. Fig. 406 shows cross-sections of a vertically cut groove, while Fig. 407 is a three-dimensional view. One way of looking at Fig. 407 is in terms of the groove walls alternately approaching each other and then receding. As the distance between the walls increases, the playback stylus sinks into the groove; as

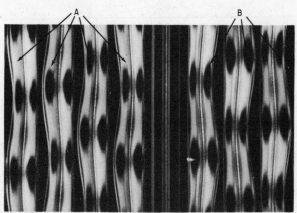

Fig. 411. *Magnified view of stereo grooves containing information only in one channel. The left wall (A) is modulated, resulting in left-channel signal when played by a 45–45 cartridge. (The right wall is straight, producing no right-channel signal). The right wall (B) is modulated, resulting in right-channel signal. (The left wall is straight, producing no left-channel signal).*

the walls come close together, the stylus is forced or pinched upward.

The Westrex system causes the playback stylus to move, not vertically or laterally when reproducing *one* channel, but at a 45° angle (Fig. 402). If the stylus reproduces *only* the left channel, it moves from bottom left to top right.

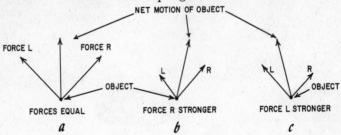

Fig. 412. *Net result of two forces acting upon an object.*

Considering just one channel for the time being, how is the groove cut to cause the playback stylus to move at an angle of 45°? Fig. 408 presents cross-sections of a groove cut in this way. Fig. 408-a shows the starting point; that is, how the groove would be cut with no signal applied to the cutting stylus. Fig. 408-b shows that the left wall has been thickened to the extent represented by the shaded area, because the cutting stylus has moved 45° upward

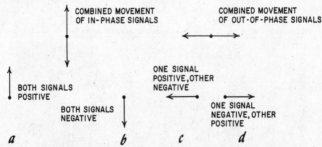

Fig. 413. *Motion of cutting stylus for various combinations of equal signal in each channel (phase difference 0° or 180°).*

and to the right. In Fig. 408-c we have the opposite situation: part of the left wall has been eaten away because the cutting stylus has moved at an angle of 45° downward to the left. Thus as the left wall becomes alternately thicker and thinner, the playback stylus is forced to move upward and downward along the right wall.

Looking head on at a record in playing position, modulation of the left wall represents the left-channel signal under the RIAA standard. Modulation of the right wall represents the signal of the right channel.

Fig. 409 is a three-dimensional view of a stereo groove which

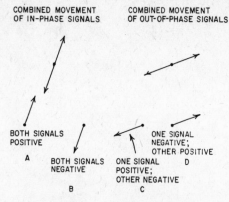

Fig. 414. *Motion of cutting stylus for various combinations of stereo signals in each channel, with the left channel being the stronger (phase difference 0° or 180°).*

contains only left-channel modulation, while Fig. 410 shows a three-dimensional view of a stereo groove containing only right-channel modulation. The successive narrowing and widening of the left wall in one case and of the right wall in the other causes

Fig. 415. *Motion of cutting stylus for equal signals in each channel, but differing in phase by 30°.*

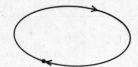

the playback stylus to move up and down at a 45° angle, either from bottom left to top right or bottom right to top left (Fig. 402). Fig. 411 is an actual photograph, greatly enlarged, of stereo grooves containing modulation for only one channel. At the left are grooves containing only left-channel signal, while at the right are grooves containing only right-channel signal. The varying shading in the photograph (light vs. dark portions) represents the vertical component. The lateral component is shown by the varying groove width.

In practice, two channels are recorded instead of just the left or right. How, then, can the cutting or playback stylus move two ways at once; that is, in the two directions shown in Fig. 402? The answer is that it doesn't. Rather, it moves in accordance with the *net result* of the signals of the two channels. Fig. 412 helps explain this. In Fig. 412-a, two forces, represented by the arrows, are shown pulling upon an object, represented by a dot; this object can be the stylus. If forces L and R are equal, the object will follow a

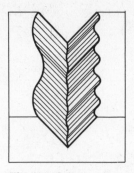

Fig. 416. *A stereo groove with different signals in each channel, i.e. in each wall.*

path that forms equal angles to each force; in Fig. 412-a, the path is straight upward. If the forces are unequal, as in Fig. 412-b, with R being the stronger, the net result is that the object moves, not

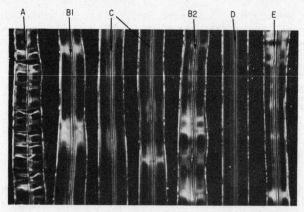

Fig. 417. *Magnified view of stereo grooves. (A) Both walls heavily modulated with a high-level signal. (B1 and B2) Both walls moderately modulated using a signal having a medium level. (C) Both walls lightly modulated by a low-level signal. (D) Neither wall modulated, representing a no-signal condition. (E) Right wall more heavily modulated. There is more signal in the right channel.*

straight upward, but at an angle to the vertical. The angle lies between 90° (vertical) and 45°. Fig. 412-c shows the net motion of the stylus when the left force is stronger.

If the cutting stylus is acted upon by equal forces in each channel, under the Westrex system it will move either straight up or straight down, or else straight to the right or left (Figs. 413-a,-b,-c,-d). The motion depends upon the phase of the signal in each channel; that is, whether the signal fed to each section of

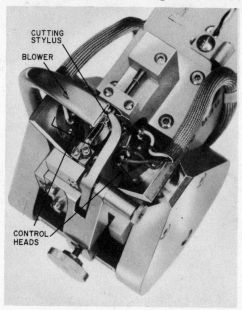

Fig. 418. *Photo of a Westrex cutter.* (Courtesy of Westrex Corp.)

the cutting head is positive-going or negative-going at a given instant. The two signals may both be positive-going, both negative-going, one positive- and one negative-going, or one negative- and the other positive-going.

Figs. 414-a,-b,-c,-d show the resultant motion of the cutting stylus if the L-channel signal is stronger than the R channel. As in Fig. 413, various combinations of phase are represented.

Whereas Figs. 413 and 414 indicate that the cutting stylus moves in a straight line at some angle to the horizontal, actually it may move in a more complex circular or elliptical pattern. Figs. 413 and 414 presume that the L and R signals are either exactly in phase (0° phase difference) or exactly out of phase with each other (180° phase difference). However, the phase difference, depending upon the microphone technique employed, may be something other than 0° or 180°. Thus, Fig. 415 shows how two signals 30° out of phase will cause the cutting stylus to move in an ellipse while recording.

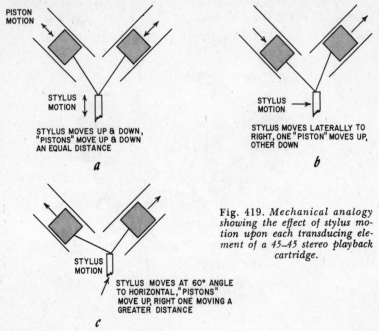

PISTON MOTION

STYLUS MOTION

STYLUS MOVES UP & DOWN, "PISTONS" MOVE UP & DOWN AN EQUAL DISTANCE

a

STYLUS MOTION

STYLUS MOVES LATERALLY TO RIGHT, ONE "PISTON" MOVES UP, OTHER DOWN

b

STYLUS MOTION

STYLUS MOVES AT 60° ANGLE TO HORIZONTAL, "PISTONS" MOVE UP, RIGHT ONE MOVING A GREATER DISTANCE

c

Fig. 419. *Mechanical analogy showing the effect of stylus motion upon each transducing element of a 45–45 stereo playback cartridge.*

The motion of the cutting stylus, which is the resultant of two signals, causes a corresponding pattern to be cut into the walls of the record groove. And this pattern is such that the left wall contains the information of channel L and the right wall that of channel R. Fig. 416 is a three-dimensional view of how a stereo groove might appear. Fig. 417 is an actual photograph of grooves in a record made under the Westrex system. A Westrex cutter is shown in Fig. 418.

The playback stylus follows the stereo groove (Fig. 416). Now the process is reversed. The motion of the playback stylus is the net result of the forces exerted by the two walls. This single net motion affects each of the two transducing elements of a stereo playback cartridge in a different manner. Hence each element of the playback cartridge produces a different signal.

This can be clarified by a mechanical analogy (Fig. 419), which in fact is not much different from the manner in which some stereo cartridges operate. Two "pistons" are shown connected to a stylus. If the stylus moves straight up and down, (Fig. 419-a), obviously both pistons will move up and down together and to an equal degree. However, if the stylus moves to the right (Fig. 419-b), then one piston goes up while the other goes down. If the

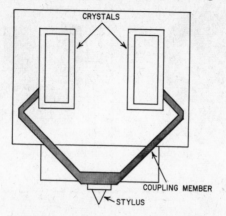

Fig. 420. *Internal view of the Ronette BF-40 stereo playback cartridge.* (Courtesy of Ronette Acoustical Corp.)

stylus moves at an angle, say 60° (Fig. 419-c), then both pistons move up, but the right piston moves farther up than the left one. Thus every type of stylus motion is resolved into a separate motion

Fig. 421. *External view of the playback cartridge of Fig. 420.* (Courtesy of Ronette Acoustical Corp.)

of each piston. In a similar manner, the motion of the stylus of the playback cartridge is resolved by each transducing element into the respective channel-L and channel-R signals.

The aptness of the mechanical analogy of Fig. 419 is shown by Fig. 420, which is the diagram of an actual stereo cartridge. The stylus motion is transferred by a coupling member to two crystals, which are piezoelectric devices. As the pressure on each crystal is varied by the coupling member, the crystal produces a corre-

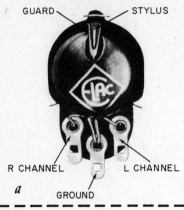

GUARD   STYLUS

R CHANNEL   L CHANNEL

GROUND

a

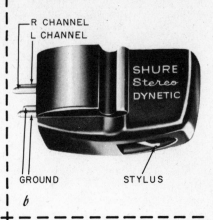

R CHANNEL
L CHANNEL

SHURE
Stereo
DYNETIC

GROUND   STYLUS

b

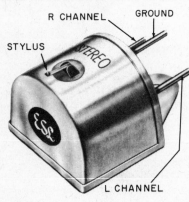

R CHANNEL   GROUND

STYLUS

STEREO

L CHANNEL

c

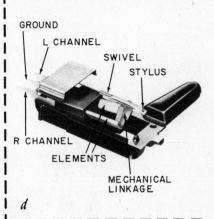

GROUND

L CHANNEL   SWIVEL

STYLUS

R CHANNEL

ELEMENTS

MECHANICAL
LINKAGE

d

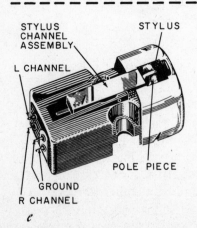

STYLUS
CHANNEL
ASSEMBLY   STYLUS

L CHANNEL

POLE PIECE

GROUND

R CHANNEL

e

Fig. 422. *Stereo cartridges. (a) Audio-gersh Corp. Stereotwin 200; (b) Shure Stereo Dynetic; (c) Electro-Sonic Laboratories C100 series Gyro/Jewel electrodynamic; (d) Electro-Voice Model 26DST; (e) General Electric magnetic variable reluctance type.*

sponding voltage. Fig. 421 is an external view of the playback cartridge represented in Fig. 420. Fig. 422 presents views of several other stereo cartridges.

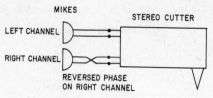

Fig. 423. *Reversing the phase of one channel so that the stereo cutter will cut an essentially lateral groove.*

Phasing

Returning to the diagram of Fig. 419-b, it can be visualized that, in recording, if one "piston" pushes while the other pulls, the

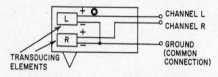

Fig. 424. *Internal wiring connections for a stereo playback cartridge to obtain proper phasing.*

*Phase as shown by + or — refers to the original signal at the microphones. Actually the output of the right transducer is out-of-phase with the left. Since the signals are reversed at the cutting head, the second reversal brings them back into phase.

cutting stylus will move laterally. This brings up an important fact: if the same signals are presented to each transducing element of the recording cartridge, but these signals are of opposite phase

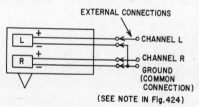

Fig. 425. *External connections for a four-terminal stereo playback cartridge to obtain proper phasing.*

—one signal negative when the other is positive—then the recording stylus makes a lateral cut. On the other hand (see Fig. 419-a), if the two signals are in phase, then the cutting stylus will inscribe a vertically modulated groove.

Ordinarily the two stereo signals will have substantial similarity to each other since, after all, they emanate from one source (although there are exceptions to this). These signals, particularly at the lower frequencies, will tend to be in phase when they reach each microphone. As a result of similar in-phase signals reaching

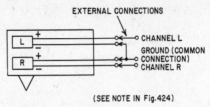

Fig. 426. *Improper external connections for a four-terminal stereo playback cartridge.*

the two transducing elements of the recording cartridge, the stylus tends to cut an essentially vertical groove. However, a number of problems of distortion and frequency response are associated with

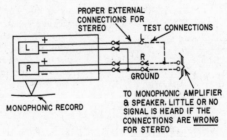

Fig. 427. *Test connections to determine whether a four-terminal stereo playback cartridge is properly phased.*

a vertically modulated groove. In other words, it is desirable to minimize the amount of vertical excursion.

If the signal of one channel is reversed in phase, which can be accomplished quite easily, as, for example, by reversing leads on one channel (Fig. 423), then the two signals are basically out of phase with each other. This, then, will produce essentially a laterally modulated groove. The RIAA has specified that "equal in-phase signals in the two channels shall result in lateral modulation of the groove." To sum up, although the original signals tend to be in phase, the leads to one of the elements of the cutting head are reversed, so that from the cutter's point of view the signals are arriving out of phase, and therefore it makes a predominantly lateral cut.

If the groove is cut laterally, then each transducing element of the playback cartridge will yield the same signal but, as can be visualized with the aid of Fig. 419, these signals will be out of phase with each other. Hence the playback cartridge restores the original situation. That is, the signals which were originally in phase but were presented to the cutting cartridge out of phase, are now again reversed in phase relative to each other, so that once more they are in-phase.

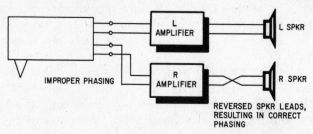

Fig. 428. *Compensating for improper phasing of the playback cartridge by reversing the speaker leads.*

So far as the user is concerned, the phase reversal accomplished by the playback cartridge may be purely automatic, or it may be necessary for him to make the proper wiring connections. Some playback cartridges have only three output terminals, and in this case the cartridge manufacturer has made the proper wiring con-

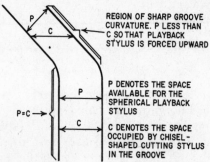

Fig. 429. *Pinch effect exerted upon the playback stylus at points of sharp groove curvature.*

nections (Fig. 424). On the other hand, some cartridges have four terminals (Fig. 425) and here it is necessary that the user make the appropriate connections so that the signal from one element of the stereo cartridge will, in the final analysis, be in phase with the signal from the other element, or, as seen from the viewpoint purely of the playback cartridge, so that the output of one element will be out of phase with the other. Fig. 426 illustrates *improper* connections.

A basic reason for providing four terminals instead of three on stereo cartridges is to permit each channel to have its own ground lead to the amplifier. This may result in less hum than if the channels shared a common ground lead. The desirability of four terminals is augmented by the CBS simplex principle for stereo amplifiers discussed in Chapter 8. This type of amplifier uses only two output tubes instead of the customary four and requires that the stereo signals be out-of-phase with each other, namely L and —R. A four-terminal cartridge permits the user to reverse the phase of one channel with respect to the other. (However, it is possible for the cartridge manufacturer to produce a three-terminal cartridge with proper out-of-phase connections for a simplex amplifier. Moreover, some stereo control amplifiers make it possible to reverse the phase of one channel with respect to the other.)

One way of telling whether the proper connections have been

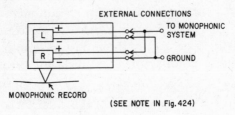

EXTERNAL CONNECTIONS

MONOPHONIC RECORD

(SEE NOTE IN Fig. 424)

Fig. 430. *Connections for playing a monophonic record with a four-terminal stereo playback cartridge.*

made with a four-terminal cartridge is to combine the two outputs (Fig. 427) and feed them into a single amplifier when the cartridge is playing a monophonic record. If phasing is wrong for stereo, then the outputs will be out of phase on a monophonic record, which contains lateral modulation, causing the signal to disappear largely or althogether.

Even though the signal from one section of the playback cartridge is taken in the wrong phase, can this not be corrected in the last stage of the audio system merely by reversing the leads to one of the speaker systems (Fig. 428)? The answer is yes, this connection can be made. However, as will be discussed in more detail in the section on stereo cartridge compatibility, the best way to play a monophonic disc with a stereo pickup is by paralleling the two outputs of the cartridge. But if these outputs are

80

phased improperly for stereo, then signal cancellation will occur in reproduction of a monophonic disc.

Compatibility

Compatibility concerns (1) the ability of monophonic cartridges to play stereo records; (2) the ability of stereo cartridges to play monophonic discs.

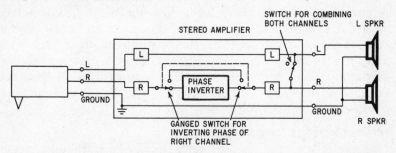

Fig. 431. *Stereo amplifier with provision for inverting the phase of one channel and then combining both channels to play monophonic records with an incorrectly phased stereo cartridge.*

Monophonic cartridge compatibility

The RIAA stereo standard requires that in-phase signals at the microphones (which contain all the audio information) shall produce a laterally cut groove on a stereo record. Hence it follows that a playback cartridge responding only to lateral groove motion would reproduce the sum of channels L and R on a stereo disc.

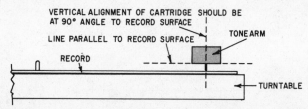

Fig. 432. *Azimuth alignment of a stereo playback cartridge with the cartridge viewed head on.*

Accordingly, a monophonic cartridge, which responds only to lateral groove motion, is compatible in the sense that it can draw the full audio information from the stereo disc, although the two channels are combined. We may say that compatibility exists in an electrical sense.

Unfortunately, most monophonic cartridges do not show compatibility in a mechanical sense. Although they are designed to have very high *lateral* compliance—ability of the stylus to move a relatively great distance in the lateral direction when slight force is applied to it by the record groove—their *vertical* compliance is quite often much smaller. True, the monophonic cartridge must have a certain amount of vertical "give" so that it can cope with the pinch effect, which tends to lift the stylus when the groove narrows at points of sharp curvature (Fig. 429). However, the vertical compliance of most cartridges is considerably less than the lateral compliance. Therefore, when the stereo groove forces the stylus upward, the stylus resists this pressure of the groove walls. If the resistance of the stylus is sufficient, the stylus tends to cut into the groove and destroy the vertical information therein. Most monophonic cartridges, or at least most of those in existence when stereo discs were first introduced in 1958, are not mechanically compatible with stereo discs.

Stereo cartridge compatibility

Generally speaking, stereo cartridges are able to play monophonic records quite satisfactorily because the stylus is free to move in the lateral direction. However, a serious problem arises with respect to rumble, chiefly due to the phonograph motor and bearings. Rumble will cause the stylus to move in both the lateral and vertical directions. Vertical rumble tends to be considerably greater—about three times as much—as lateral rumble. Hence, in playing a monophonic disc, a cartridge that has high vertical compliance (enabling it to respond to vertical rumble) reproduces substantially more rumble than a cartridge with low vertical compliance.

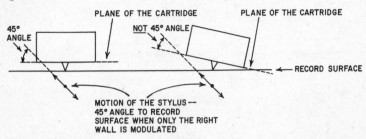

Fig. 433. *Crosstalk due to azimuth misalignment of a stereo playback cartridge.*

To circumvent this problem of vertical rumble when playing a mono disc with a stereo pickup, it is desirable to combine both outputs of the cartridge so that they are additive with respect to lateral (audio) information and cancelling with respect to vertical (rumble) information (Fig. 430). Such a connection involves a phasing which is the same as for stereo (Fig. 427). A very simple switch could be installed to link the left and right outputs. for playing monophonic discs. To allow for incorrect cartridge phasing, it is possible to provide means in the stereo amplifier for reversing the phase of one channel at an intermediate stage in

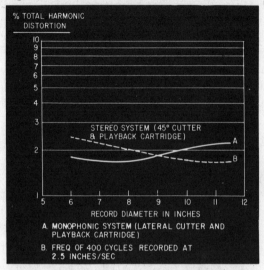

Fig. 434. *Comparison of total harmonic distortion between a monophonic system and one channel of a stereo system—recording and playback.*

the amplifier and subsequently adding the two channels (Fig. 431).

Of course it is possible to take the signal only from one section of a stereo cartridge when playing a monophonic disc, but this fails to take advantage of the possibilities for cancellation of vertical rumble. Also, the signal-to-noise ratio will be poorer because less signal is presented by the stereo cartridge to the amplifier when only one element is used.

Crosstalk

One problem of stereo reproduction by means of discs is crosstalk—the appearance of the sound of one channel in the other. Crosstalk occurs in the cutting head, in the record groove and in the playback cartridges.

Generally it is possible to maintain an overall crosstalk ratio of better than 20 db over much of the audio range; that is, the ratio of the audio signal which properly belongs in a given channel to the audio signal which also appears there but belongs in the other channel is more than 10 to 1. Data as to the amount of crosstalk in the entire system, using both a Westrex cutting head and a Westrex reproducer, show a crosstalk ratio of about 22.5 db at 1,000 cycles, about 20 db at 4,000 cycles and thereafter progressively worsening. The ratio is about 16 db at 7,000 cycles, about 9 db at 10,000 and less than 5 db at about 12,000 cycles. Thereafter it improves but remains less than 10 db up to 15,000 cycles. However, in the range which seems to be essentially responsible for the stereo effect, up to 8,000 cycles, crosstalk appears to be low enough so that the sound of each channel is maintained sufficiently distinct for practical purposes.

To minimize crosstalk in playback, it is important to maintain vertical alignment of the stylus with respect to the record surface

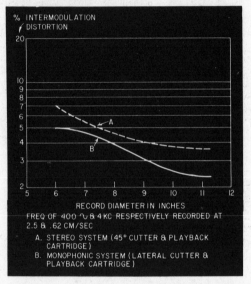

Fig. 435. *Comparison of intermodulation distortion between a monophonic system and one channel of a stereo system—recording and playback.* (Courtesy of Westrex Corp.)

(Fig. 432). This is sometimes referred to as azimuth alignment. If the stylus inclines to the left or right, this introduces the sound of one channel into the other. It also causes distortion because the stylus is less free to move to one side than to the other.

Fig. 433 helps explain why crosstalk is caused by vertical misalignment of the playback stylus. Assume that only the right wall of the groove is modulated, so that there should be output only from one section of the cartridge, the right channel, because the stylus moves at a 45° angle. But if the stylus is misaligned vertically, it will not move exactly at a 45° angle with reference to the *plane of the cartridge*. Therefore the left channel will also contain some signal output, which can only be the signal belonging to the right channel.

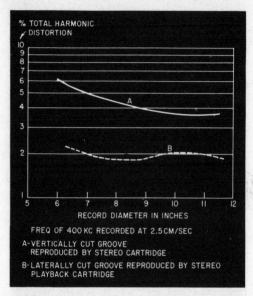

Fig. 436. *Comparison of total harmonic distortion for reproduction of vertically and laterally modulated grooves by a stereo playback cartridge.* (Courtesy of Westrex Corp.)

Distortion

The more complex characteristic of a stereo groove as compared with a monophonic (lateral) one raises the problem of more severe distortion on the stereo disc. Fig. 434 compares harmonic distortion at 400 cycles at a velocity of 2.5 cm/sec (a fairly moderate signal level) between a mono and a stereo system. The monophonic record has been cut laterally and reproduced by a lateral cartridge (Westrex). In the stereo system, the record has been cut in stereo fashion for just one channel (comparison can be made only for one channel) and the cutting head and stereo reproducer are Westrex models.

Fig. 434 indicates that, on the whole, harmonic distortion is not much different in the two systems. The monophonic system produces more distortion on the outer part of the record, where diameter is large, and less distortion on the inner part.

However, the story is different with respect to intermodulation distortion, which is considerably more offensive to the ear than harmonic distortion. Fig. 435 compares the IM distortion of mono-phonic and stereo systems, using frequencies of 400 and 4,000 cycles, respectively, recorded at 2.5 and 0.62 cm/sec. Throughout the groove diameter, the IM distortion is greater for the stereo system.

To the extent that the stereo disc causes the stylus to move

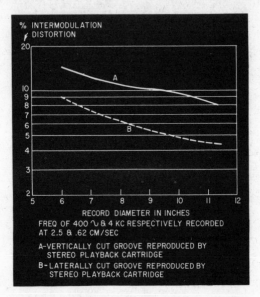

Fig. 437. *Comparison of intermodulation distor-tion for reproduction of vertically and laterally modulated grooves by a stereo playback cartridge.* (Courtesy of Westrex Corp.)

vertically rather than in lateral or 45° fashion, there is a sharp increase in harmonic and IM distortion (Figs. 436 and 437). The solid lines in Figs. 436 and 437 show distortion when a stereo cartridge reproduces a vertically cut groove. The dash lines in those figures show the much lower distortion when a stereo cart-ridge reproduces a laterally cut groove.

These two illustrations reveal one of the principal reasons why the RIAA has recommended that in-phase signals should be recorded so as to produce a laterally cut groove: distortion will be much smaller for a lateral than a vertical groove.

Rumble

In analyzing compatibility, we have previously mentioned that, due to motor and bearing imperfections, there is low-frequency vibration in the motion of the turntable, which becomes apparent as rumble when picked up by the playback cartridge. Rumble exists both in the vertical and lateral modes, with vertical rumble being as much as three times greater. Hence the stereo cartridge, which responds considerably more to vertical motion than does the typical monophonic pickup, produces a good deal more rumble signal. Therefore, in playing stereo or mono discs with a stereo cartridge, greater stress must be placed upon a rumble-free phonograph than in the case of monophonic cartridges.

A number of stereo cartridges seek to cope with the problem of vertical rumble by attenuating the response of the cartridge, at low frequencies, to vertical stylus motion. In some cases this is done by electrical means, using capacitors and resistors to filter the low-frequency content of vertical stylus motion. In other cases, mechanical techniques are employed to attenuate the response of the cartridge to vertical motion at low frequencies, as, for example, by the use of springs. However, such attempts have tended to degrade the quality of the stereo sound and to introduce additional crosstalk between channels.

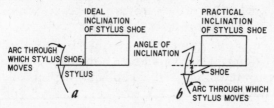

a STYLUS MOTION IS VERTICALLY PERPENDICULAR TO SURFACE OF RECORD IN RESPONSE TO VERTICALLY MODULATED GROOVE.

b STYLUS MOTION IS AT AN ANGLE TO PERPENDICULAR IN RESPONSE TO VERTICALLY MODULATED GROOVE.

Fig. 438. *Effect of angle of inclination of stylus shoe upon stylus motion.*

Characteristics of the playback cartridge

Just as the success of a conventional high-fidelity system is in large part dependent upon the quality of the phono pickup, so it is with stereo. There are a considerable number of stereo cartridges at various prices and of various designs, and they do not all help to an equal degree to realize the potentialities of the stereo disc.

Because of the complex nature of the stereo groove, a stylus with a relatively fine tip is required to trace it. Although quite adequate for monophonic records, a tip with a radius of 1 mil

(1/1,000 inch) is too coarse for the stereo disc. At first, a 0.7 mil radius was considered suitable for stereo, but upon further investigation the RIAA recommended that the radius be 0.5 mil for satisfactory tracing.

Reducing the radius of the stylus tip from 1 to 0.5 mil—that is, by half—reduces the area of the tip to one-fourth of its previous size, since area varies with the square of the radius. For a given tracking force—pressure exerted by the stylus upon the record—there is now four times as much pressure upon the groove per unit of area. Increased groove wear results unless tracking force is reduced to a corresponding degree. Whereas tracking forces of about 6 to 8 grams are considered tolerable for a monophonic cartridge, tracking forces of about 2 grams or less are required for a stereo pickup employing a 0.5-mil stylus. But at 2 grams or less tracking force, keeping the stylus within the groove on loud passages requires a stylus with the ability to move readily under slight pressure and a well-balanced, virtually frictionless tone arm.

Summarizing, reducing the radius of the stylus tip to permit adequate tracking of the complex stereo groove in turn requires a lighter tracking force, which in turn places a greater premium upon a high-quality cartridge and tone arm.

Two essential requirements of any high-quality cartridge are low mass and high compliance. Low mass permits extended high-frequency response. High compliance permits adequate low-frequency response.

Plastic resonance

The mass of the cartridge stylus and those elements to which it is attached, together with the groove wall (which has a certain amount of "give") form a resonant system; this is referred to as "plastic resonance." At the resonant frequency, response is exaggerated or peaked. Above the resonant frequency, response declines sharply. Hence it is desirable that the frequency of plastic resonance occurs above the audio range or at least not much lower than 15,000 cycles. The smaller the dynamic mass of the stylus, the higher the resonant frequency. In several of the finest monophonic cartridges, stylus mass has been kept sufficiently low to move plastic resonance comfortably outside the audio range. In a stereo cartridge, the problem of holding stylus mass to a sufficiently small value is increased because the stylus has to drive not one transducing element but two. The stylus and its attached elements are more complex, involving more parts, and the stylus mass therefore tends to be greater than for a monophonic cartridge of equivalent quality.

The compliance of the stylus denotes how far it can be moved by a given amount of force. In reproducing low frequencies, the stylus has to describe movements of considerable amplitude. High compliance enables the stylus to move easily and reproduce the low frequencies with low distortion. Low compliance causes the

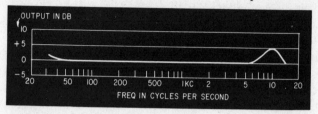

Fig. 439. *Frequency response of Westrex stereo playback cartridge after RIAA frequency equalization.* (Courtesy of Westrex Corp.)

stylus to resist movement. Therefore it reproduces low frequencies with considerable distortion or possibly not at all—it may jump out of the groove that it is unable to follow. The greater complexity of design of a stereo cartridge makes it more difficult to achieve the high compliance of a first-rate monophonic cartridge; consequently good low-frequency response is harder to achieve.

Symmetry

An important factor in the design of a stereo cartridge is sym-

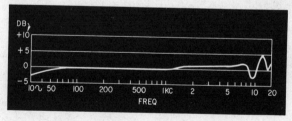

Fig. 440. *Recorded frequency characteristic of Westrex stereo cutter.* (Courtesy of Westrex Corp.)

metry. Each transducing element should have virtually the same output level and the same characteristics with respect to frequency response, distortion, etc. Otherwise the stereo effect suffers.

Since a stereo groove is modulated vertically as well as laterally, the greater depth of the groove compared with a monophonic one would result in a wider groove if the same signal level were recorded as on mono discs. To avoid this—a wider groove which would diminish the playing time—it is necessary to use a lower recording level on stereo discs—3 db less on each channel. This increases the problem of the phono pickup presenting enough signal to the amplifier to result in a satisfactorily high ratio between signal and amplifier noise on each channel.

The smaller amount of signal recorded on each wall of the stereo groove necessarily reduces the ratio between audio signal and groove noise. Hence greater emphasis must be placed upon low-noise record materials and upon the user keeping the grooves free of dust, lint, etc., which help produce noise.

As illustrated in Fig. 438, the shoe that holds the stylus is not exactly parallel with the record surface but forms an angle of several degrees. This may be referred to as the angle of inclination. Because the stylus shoe slopes, the stylus does not move truly up and down; instead its motion is at a slight angle to the vertical. In other words, the vertical modulation in the stereo groove causes the stylus, *in relative terms,* to move back and forth along the groove. Hence the vertical motion of the stylus modulates the response of the stylus to lateral information in the groove, introducing distortion akin to flutter in a conventional phono system

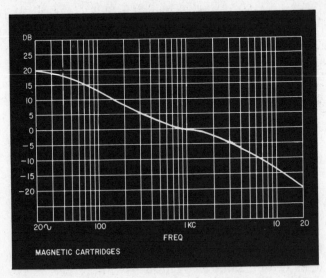

Fig. 441. *RIAA playback equalization.*

or in a tape machine. However, if the angle of inclination is the same in the cutting head and in the playback cartridge, this distortion cancels. Therefore the attempt is made to have the same angle of inclination for the stylus of the cutting head as for the stylus of the playback cartridge.

Frequency response

The preceding discussion has indicated that there are serious problems of maintaining adequate bass and treble response in a stereo disc system; nevertheless the problems are not insuperable.

Fig. 439 portrays the frequency response of the Westrex playback cartridge, as an example of what a high-quality unit can achieve. The low-frequency response is excellent, and, although a peak does occur at the high end in the region of 10,000 cycles, this peak is kept below 5 db. There is a slight rise at the extreme low end, which Westrex attributes to the resonance of the arm mass with the stylus compliance.

Fig. 440 indicates the approximate recorded frequency characteristic, using a Westrex cutting head. To some extent, the peak in playback response at the high end is cancelled by the dip in the recorded characteristic, so that the overall response of a system using Westrex equipment would be relatively smooth.

The tone arm presents a problem of maintaining adequate low-frequency response when the stylus moves vertically. For monophonic reproduction, tone arms have been designed so that they can follow the relatively gradual ups and down due to such factors as record warp and foreign matter in the groove. If the arm moves in response to vertical forces, the cartridge follows, so that the stylus does *not* move relative to the cartridge; this occurs only at low frequencies. But in the case of a stereo reproducer, it is necessary that the stylus move relative to the cartridge mechanism to reproduce vertical groove information. Therefore the tone arm should have the same characteristics for vertical and lateral motion, permitting equally good low frequency response for vertical or lateral groove modulation. Many tone arms that are satisfactory for monophonic discs (lateral groove modulation) are not usable for the reproduction of vertical groove modulation at low frequencies.

Equalization

The problem of varying equalization characteristics that plagued LP records in their early years (through 1954) will not be repeated in stereo. RIAA equalization (Fig. 441) has been accepted as the standard for all stereo discs, or at least those made according to the Westrex system.

However, the fact that there are standard recording and playback equalization characteristics does not eliminate all problems of achieving correct equalization on the user's part. It is still necessary, when using a magnetic playback cartridge, to insure that the control amplifier contains *accurate* RIAA equalization, not just a loose approximation, and that the equalization be virtually identical for each channel. Otherwise each channel will have a different frequency response characteristic, tending to impair the stereo effect.

Achieving accurate equalization is more difficult with piezo-electric, ceramic or crystal pickups. These cartridges are essentially self-equalizing and, having a relatively high output, are ordinarily intended to be fed into a high-level input jack (the same kind of jack as used, say, for a tuner). But the bass response of the piezoelectric cartridge will be flat only if the control amplifier places the correct resistance across the cartridge. Too low a load resistance will cut bass response, while too high a resistance will exaggerate bass response. Typically, a load resistance of about 2,000,000 ohms is proper; one or two cartridges on the market (as of 1958) will work satisfactorily with load resistances as low as 510,000 ohms. Consequently, the user of a piezoelectric cartridge must ascertain the required load resistance and check whether his control amplifier provides this value. If not, the necessary change should be made in the control amplifier, a simple matter for the technician or for the technically proficient audiophile.

Sometimes the control amplier treats the piezoelectric cartridge not as a high-output device, but instead uses an electrical network to convert the cartridge into a low-output device having the same frequency response characteristic as a magnetic cartridge and therefore requiring the same playback equalization. However, such a network may be appropriate for one piezoelectric pickup and not for another. Some manufacturers supply a network suitable for their cartridge in the form of an adapter placed between the cartridge and the input jack of the control amplifier.

stereo on discs— other systems

THE three remaining categories of stereo disc systems may be classified from the viewpoint of how the two channels are incorporated into the groove: 1. dual-groove; 2. single-groove, two-dimensional (vertical–lateral systems); 3. single-groove, one-dimensional (carrier-frequency systems).

Dual-groove systems

Two dual-groove systems have been proposed. One, the Cook system, has been in actual commercial use, while the other, the Weil system, has never passed the proposal stage.

Cook system

The first stereo disc system available to the public in this country was that of Emory Cook, introduced in 1952. As illustrated in Fig. 501, each channel is recorded on a separate band of grooves. A

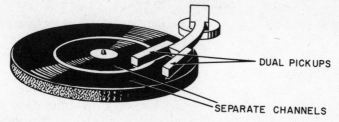

Fig. 501. *In the Cook system, each channel is recorded separately on a single disc.*

special tone arm accommodating two cartridges side by side is needed. The distance between the styli must be *exactly* the same as the distance between the starting grooves on each band, a requirement not easy to meet.

Although the Cook system was used by a relatively small number of audiophiles for a few years, three basic shortcomings led to its eventual demise.

1. It was difficult to coordinate the two cartridges so that their styli would simultaneously land in the starting grooves on each band, and almost impossible at any point after that. Hence one could not cue to a point part way in a selection.

2. The burden of a tone arm carrying two cartridges made it difficult to employ the Cook system in record changers.

3. The dual-groove technique was wasteful permitting only half as much recording time per side as a mono disc or the single-groove stereo systems. About 10 to 15 minutes could be recorded

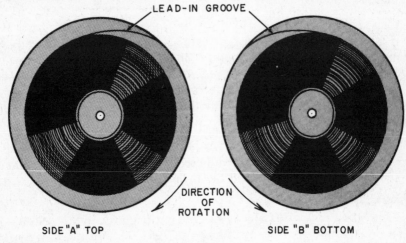

LEAD-IN GROOVE

DIRECTION OF ROTATION

SIDE "A" TOP   SIDE "B" BOTTOM

Fig. 502. *The Weil system proposed recording one channel on each side of a phonograph disc.*

on one side of a Cook record compared with 25 to 30 minutes on others. Whereas 25 to 30 minutes of time makes it possible to present many symphonies, concertos, etc. complete on one side of a record, having 10 to 15 minutes means that for many standard works the listener must turn over the record. Moreover, in the Cook system, the listener would for a second time have to go through the careful process of positioning the styli to fall into the correct grooves.

The Weil system

The Weil system affords the user no more playing time *per*

record than the Cook system, but it does allow him the customary playing time of about 25 to 30 minutes before having to reposition the cartridges. Although never put into commercial use, the system was proposed by a leading figure in the phonograph industry, Maximilian Weil, and deserves a brief description.

The Weil system (Fig. 502) would record one channel on the top side of the record and the second on the underside. Two tone

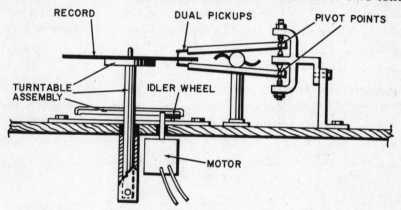

Fig. 503. *A rather complex mechanism would be required to play back a disc cut by the Weil method.*

arms and their respective cartridges would simultaneously play the two sides of the record (Fig. 503). Each arm, Weil states:

"has its own base pivotally mounted, and the two can be locked to operate in unison or they can be operated independently to permit the use of the upper arm and pickup to play normal LP discs."[1]

Behind Weil's proposal is the argument that other stereo disc systems, apart from Cook's, involve a sacrifice in terms of distortion. His system would maintain all the advantages of monophonic recording and reproducing techniques, at the same time permitting stereo reproduction. He states:

"It took 75 years to achieve the clarity, the cleanness, the refinement of today's LP discs. At this juncture, the question is then, 'Is the music lover willing to sacrifice all that for a measure of spatial effect?' "[2]

In Weil's system, conventional monophonic recording equipment and techniques would be employed, using two turntables

[1] Maximilian Weil, "New Approach to Stereo Records," *Audio*, June, 1958.
[2] *Ibid.*

to make two master lacquers for the two channels. After each is processed, the recordings would be synchronized and pressed so that the starting points on the opposite sides of the disc correspond.

Vertical-lateral systems

Whereas in the Westrex system each transducing element responds to 45° motion of the stylus, in a number of other systems, vertical and lateral stylus motion actuates the transducing elements. Three of these—the London and Sugden, CBS, and EMI systems—provide true stereo, while a fourth, the data signal method, is a quasi-stereo process.

London and Sugden system

In 1957, London and Sugden in England announced the successful development of vertical—lateral systems. As illustrated in Fig. 504, the record is cut so that one channel causes vertical

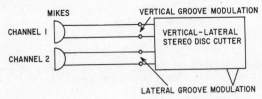

Fig. 504. *Vertical–lateral method of cutting stereo discs.*

modulation of the groove and the other horizontal modulation. (See also Figs. 404, 405, 406 and 407 beginning on page 66 in Chapter 4).

To the extent that the signals in each channel are the same in waveform and amplitude, the net result of applying such signals to the control elements of the cutter is that the cutting stylus moves diagonally; that is, at a 45° angle to the horizontal. The principle involved was explained in connection with Fig. 412-a, which, shows that, if two forces pull upon an object at 45° angles to the horizontal, the object will move vertically. In the same way, if one force is lateral and the other vertical, the object will move at a 45° angle.

The resulting groove under the Sugden and London systems is the same as a groove recorded under the Westrex system but containing modulation only for one channel (Figs. 409 and 410). In other words, under the London and Sugden method, only one wall of the groove contains modulation when there are *equal* signals in both channels.

One of the transducing elements of the playback cartridge is designed to respond to lateral stylus motion and the other to vertical. If the stylus moves at a 45° angle, both of the transducing elements are actuated and produce equal signals.

To the extent that the signal in one channel is stronger than in the other, groove modulation will tend to be essentially vertical

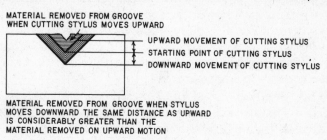

MATERIAL REMOVED FROM GROOVE
WHEN CUTTING STYLUS MOVES UPWARD

— UPWARD MOVEMENT OF CUTTING STYLUS
— STARTING POINT OF CUTTING STYLUS
— DOWNWARD MOVEMENT OF CUTTING STYLUS

MATERIAL REMOVED FROM GROOVE WHEN STYLUS
MOVES DOWNWARD THE SAME DISTANCE AS UPWARD
IS CONSIDERABLY GREATER THAN THE
MATERIAL REMOVED ON UPWARD MOTION

Fig. 505. *Different amounts of material are removed from the record during upward and downward movements of a vertical cutting stylus.*

or essentially lateral, depending upon which channel is stronger. If the net groove modulation is largely vertical, a serious problem of distortion *tends* to be introduced in the cutting process. Vertical modulation inherently produces more distortion than lateral modulation in cutting (Fig. 505). When the stylus moves downward, it must remove more groove material than when it moves upward. More force must be used to move the cutting stylus downward than an equal distance upward. Conversely, for

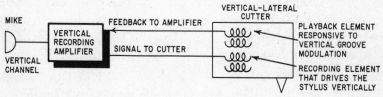

Fig. 506. *The use of feedback to minimize distortion in vertical groove cutting.*

a given force, corresponding to the audio signal, the stylus will not move as far downward as it will move upward. Failure to move equal distances for equal amounts of signal results in distortion. This situation does not occur in lateral recording, where the cutting stylus moves from side to side, meeting an equal amount of resistance in each direction.

97

Much of the distortion in cutting a vertical groove can be eliminated by feedback techniques. As the stylus meets increased resistance in making the downward cut, a proportional signal is fed back to the driving amplifier (Fig. 506). The feedback causes the amplifier to produce a greater amount of power for driving the stylus. However, feedback does not remove all the distortion.

At best, under the London and Sugden systems, a 45° groove results only when equal signals appear in each channel. In the Westrex system, such signals produce a laterally modulated groove. As was shown in Fig. 435, there is appreciably less intermodulation distortion for a laterally cut groove than for one cut at an angle of 45°. Hence the Westrex system appears to have an advantage over the vertical–lateral techniques.

Another disadvantage of the London–Sugden method is that the vertical channel tends to produce a signal due to pinch effect in the lateral channel. As was illustrated in Fig. 429, at points of rapid lateral motion in the groove it narrows, forcing the stylus upward. This periodic vertical motion of the stylus manifests itself as an audio signal in the vertical channel. In the Westrex system, however, the pinch effect appears in both channels in equal amounts, which is less disturbing to the illusion than such an aberration appearing only in one channel.

In similar fashion, the problem of achieving adequate low-frequency response due to tone-arm compliance (Chapter 4) affects only one channel of the vertical–lateral systems, whereas the effect is symmetrical in the Westrex.

All in all, although the Westrex and vertical–lateral systems in certain respects suffer from the same problems, it is considered preferable to divide them between two channels instead of concentrating them into one. The division helps to preserve the stereo effect to a higher degree.

CBS system

As discussed in Chapter 4, stereo discs are not compatible with a number of monophonic cartridges because the latter have insufficient vertical compliance or too much dynamic mass vertically so that the stylus plows through the record material on vertical excursions instead of rising and falling as it should. For compatibility, as well as to simplify the problems of cutting a stereo groove, the Columbia Broadcasting System Laboratories developed a method of recording designed to minimize vertical modulation to the extent that the stylus of the average monophonic pickup would have no difficulty in following vertical excursions. The method uses a vertical–lateral cutting technique that imposes less demands upon the cutter than a 45/45 technique. At the same time, the CBS stereo disc is meant to be played back by the standard 45/45 cartridge.

Fig. 507 shows how recording takes place. The left-channel signal, L, and the right-channel signal, R, are combined in a

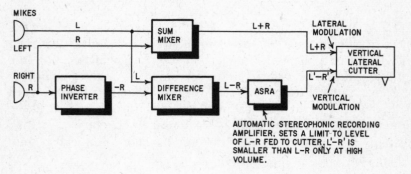

Fig. 507. *The basic elements of the CBS stereo recording system.*

mixer to produce a sum signal, L + R. The sum signal is fed to the vertical–lateral cutter to produce lateral modulation of the groove. The R signal is inverted 180°, producing what we may call —R. L and —R are combined in another mixer to form L — R, which is termed a difference signal. L — R is fed into a special automatic stereo recording amplifier, called ASRA for short, which feeds the difference signal to the vertical element of the cutter to produce vertical groove modulation.

The ASRA reduces the intensity of the L — R signal so that vertical groove modulation will be compatible with monophonic pickups, yet will retain sufficient stereo information so as not to alter significantly the stereo effect. Depending upon the intensity of the difference signal and the frequencies appearing in it, ASRA limits its amplitude. ASRA is in the nature of an electronic computer, whose contents and exact mode of operation have not been disclosed. CBS has stated only that, on the basis of studies of the nature of stereophonic sound:

"the minimum amount of difference signal was determined

which was needed to achieve full stereophonic effect as a function of the frequency and of intensity."[3]

However, one commentator has noted that:

"at low levels, up to about 20 db below maximum output of the system, the difference (signal) is unchanged . . . But for the top 20 db of dynamic range, the ASRA gets busy and changes the difference (signal) so that the vertical excursion never exceeds the desired figure of .0002 inch."[4]

To review the recording process, the lateral channel contains the full audio information, L + R. The stereophonic characteristics of this information appear in the vertical channel, consisting of L — R. In the following explanation, we shall see how the sum and difference signals are recombined to produce a distinct L signal and a distinct R signal. We shall assume a low recorded volume level, so that vertical modulation consists of L — R at the original intensity instead of at a reduced level; that is, we shall assume the ASRA control function has not been called into operation.

By using a 45/45 cartridge for playback, the L signal automatically appears in the output of one transducing element and the R signal in the other. This can be explained with the aid of a mechanical analogy (Figs. 508 and 509). The piston-like blocks in these figures represent the mechanical motion in each transducing element that results from the lateral or vertical movement of the playback stylus.

In Fig. 508 we see the effect of lateral stylus movement upon the transducing elements of the 45/45 cartridge. As the stylus goes to the right, the "piston" of element L moves down, while the "piston" of element R moves up. As the stylus moves to the left, the opposite takes place, with piston L moving up and piston R going down. In brief, the mechanical motion, and therefore the electrical output, of element L is opposite in phase to element R. Consequently, when element L produces an L + R signal (in response to lateral stylus motion), element R produces a signal of opposite phase, —L — R.

---

[3] Peter C. Goldmark, Benjamin B. Bauer, William S. Bachman, "The Columbia Compatible Stereophonic Record." Paper delivered at the Institute of Radio Engineers Convention, March 25, 1958.

[4] Norman H. Crowhurst, "Compatibility and the Stereo Disc," RADIO-ELECTRONICS Magazine, August, 1958.

The effect of vertical motion upon each transducing element of a 45/45 cartridge is shown in Fig. 509. In this case the pistons

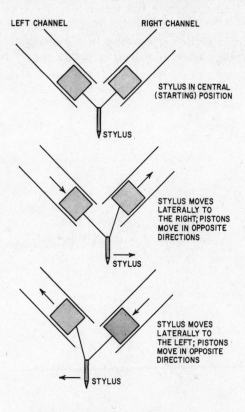

LEFT CHANNEL   RIGHT CHANNEL

STYLUS IN CENTRAL
(STARTING) POSITION

STYLUS

STYLUS MOVES
LATERALLY TO
THE RIGHT; PISTONS
MOVE IN OPPOSITE
DIRECTIONS

STYLUS

STYLUS MOVES
LATERALLY TO
THE LEFT; PISTONS
MOVE IN OPPOSITE
DIRECTIONS

STYLUS

Fig. 508. *A mechanical analogy showing the effects of lateral stylus motion on the transducing element in each channel of a 45/45 playback cartridge.*

move up or down together. The mechanical motion and the electrical outputs of the two elements are in phase. Thus each produces the L — R signal contained in the vertical component of groove modulation.

Table 5–1 shows how the signal information produced by element L adds, and the same for element R. For element L, the L + R signal is added to the L — R signal, producing 2L (that is, +R and —R cancel, leaving only L information). For element R, the —L —R signal is added to the L — R signal, producing —2R. In aggregate, element L produces only L information, and element R produces only R information; these signals are fed to the left and right channels, respectively, of the stereo system. Since the R information is out of phase with the L information, this requires that the phase of one of the elements of the stereo

Table 5—1. The signals appearing in the elements of a 45/45 cartridge when reproducing a CBS stereo disc

transducing element for left channel	transducing element for right channel
L + R	— L — R
L — R	L — R
2L	—2R

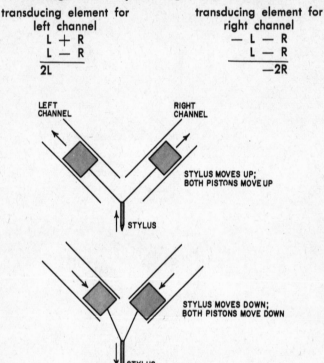

Fig. 509. *The effects of vertical stylus motion upon the transducing element in each channel of a 45/45 playback cartridge.*

cartridge be reversed (Fig. 510). The phasing is the same as if a disc recorded under the 45/45 system were being played (Figs. 424 and 425).

We have been assuming that the difference signal L — R is of relatively small magnitude so that ASRA has not reduced it. Now, however, suppose that L — R is reduced by ASRA to a level which we may call L′ — R′. Then, in playback, each transducing element of the cartridge does not produce purely an L or R signal. To illustrate, assume ASRA converts L — R to half its original value, 0.5 (L − R). Therefore, in playback, the cartridge causes element L to subtract 0.5 (L − R) from L + R. The result is

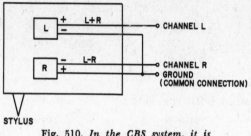

Fig. 510. *In the CBS system, it is necessary to reverse the phase of one of the elements of the playback cartridge.*

1.5L + 0.5R. In other words, the signal ouput of the L element is dominantly but not altogether the L signal. Similarly, the signal

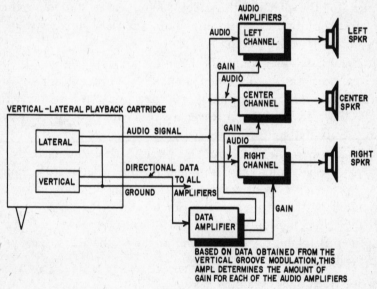

Fig. 511. *The data signal quasi-stereo system is similar to coded stereo in some respects.*

output of the R element, after phase inversion, is 1.5R + 0.5L; that is, dominantly R. The dominance of L in one channel and of R in the other is sufficient to preserve the stereo effect.

In recording, the L and R signals ordinarily have a fair degree of similarity inasmuch as the two stereo microphones pick up sound from the same originating source. Because of this similarity, the difference signal L — R inherently tends to be smaller than the sum signal L + R. Even without ASRA, the vertical component of the record groove, containing L — R, tends to be smaller than if just the L or just the R signal were recorded vertically. But ASRA further insures that vertical groove modulation is kept within the prescribed limits.

Data signal system

Also associated with the name of EMI in England is a quasi-stereo technique claimed to provide worth-while results. As illustrated in Fig. 511, all the sound (signal) is recorded as lateral groove modulation, while the vertical modulation comprises information (data) concerning the direction (speaker) from which the sound should issue. Using two or three speakers, a special amplifier decides from the data fed to it by the vertical-responsive element of the playback cartridge what speaker should produce the most sound at every instant. Thus the data signal system is very similar to coded stereo.

In recording, the information for the vertical contents of the stereo groove can be obtained manually by having a musically trained technician control an appropriate signal as he follows the score. This can be done on the basis of a tape recording instead of at the original performance.

It is also possible to obtain the vertical data automatically by placing special microphones to determine whether the sound issues principally from the left or the right. The audio signals generated by these microphones can be converted to the type of electrical information required to inform the special playback amplifier as to the relative volume of sound that each speaker is supposed to produce.

Carrier-frequency systems

In essence, in a carrier-frequency system all the audio frequencies of one channel are cut laterally into the groove. A superaudible frequency (the carrier) is modulated by the audio frequencies of the second channel, and the modulated carrier is also cut laterally into the groove. In playback, a monophonic pickup is used. A basic requirement is that it have extremely good high-frequency response to reproduce the modulated carrier frequency, which is superaudible (say 30,000 cycles). The signal generated by the playback cartridge is fed into one channel of the stereo system. To obtain the other channel, the carrier frequency is separated from the audio frequencies, then the audio information of the second channel is extracted from the carrier by a detector circuit.

Minter system

The Minter system is a refined version of the carrier-frequency technique, incorporating the principle and advantages of using sum and difference frequencies as in the CBS disc system and in the Crosby multiplex system of broadcasting. The total audio information, which may be called L + R, is recorded laterally. The stereo information, L − R, is recorded by modulating a superaudible carrier frequency. Since there is no vertical modulation of the groove, this type of stereo record is truly compatible in the sense that it can be played by any conventional cartridge for monophonic purposes. For stereo reproduction, a monophonic pickup is still suitable, provided it has adequate high-frequency response.

The Minter system uses a 25,000-cycle carrier. Although only a very few conventional pickups have a response extending this high, proponents of the system have felt that cartridge manufacturers would face fewer problems in making such a cartridge than in meeting the rigorous design requirements of a two-dimensional pickup responding either to 45/45 or vertical–lateral groove modulation and incorporating two transducing elements with minimum crosstalk, low distortion, extended high-frequency response, good low-frequency response, etc.

Compatibility

The Minter system is compatible in that it permits stereo discs to be reproduced by a monophonic pickup and provides completely satisfactory sound if the signal from the pickup is fed directly to a monophonic sound system. Moreover, compatibility exists in the recording process for a cutter of radically new design is not required. However, it must have relatively smooth response to about 30,000 cycles.

It is claimed that the Minter system achieves between 30- and 40-db separation between channels, compared with about 20 db for other systems. Moreover, azimuth (vertical) alignment of the stylus is not as critical as in the case of the two-dimensional groove, where such misalignment increases crosstalk and distortion. The fact that the Minter system employs a playback cartridge with only one transducing element instead of two lightens the problems of keeping mass low, compliance high and keeping resonance above the audio range.

Fig. 512 shows in basic terms the recording process used by Minter. The R signal is inverted 180° in phase to produce −R. The latter is combined with the L signal in a "difference mixer" to obtain L − R. The L − R signal is fed to a frequency modulator, where it modulates the 25-kc carrier. The modulated

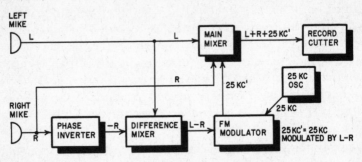

Fig. 512. *Recording setup for the Minter stereo system.*

carrier may be referred to as 25 kc'. The 25 kc' goes to a "main mixer" to be combined with the L and R signals. Hence the total output of the main mixer is L + R + 25 kc'. Remember that 25 kc' is 25 kc modulated by L − R. The total output is fed into the record cutter, which inscribes a lateral groove.

Playback

Fig. 513 shows the elements of the playback process. The playback cartridge picks up the combined signal, L + R + 25 kc', which is fed to a special preamplifier. A filter selects the 25 kc' component which goes to an FM detector which extracts the L − R signal. The L − R information is fed to the "left mixer," where it is combined with the composite L + R + 25 kc' signal. The net result is 2L + 25 kc' because the R and −R signals cancel. This goes to the left channel of the stereo system. Although the 25 kc' component is present, it is too high in frequency to be audible. Moreover, in the preamplifier the signal is subject to the usual RIAA treble de-emphasis, which greatly reduces its magnitude.

The L − R signal turned out by the FM detector goes to a phase inverter, where it becomes R − L. This is combined in the "right mixer" with the L + R + 25 kc′ signal to produce 2R + 25 kc′, which is then fed to the left channel of the stereo system.

The L + R signal fed to the record cutter contains frequencies to about 15,000 cycles. However, the L − R signal, which modulates the 25-kc carrier, is limited to about 8,000 or 10,000 cycles. This prevents the modulated carrier from interfering with the

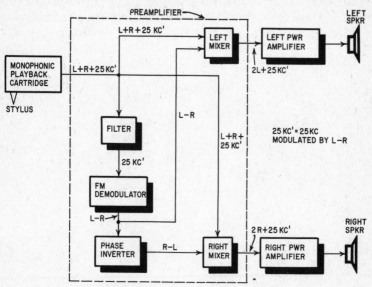

Fig. 513. *The basic elements required to play back a Minter stereo recording.*

audio frequencies. However, the stereo effect, which is contained in the L − R signal, does not depend very much upon frequencies above 8,000 cycles or so.

Because of the very high frequencies that must be recorded on the disc under the Minter system, there is increased danger that in playback the stylus may skip out of the groove on sharp turns, due to high frequencies recorded at high amplitudes. Therefore the recording level is kept about 3 to 4 db less than on a monophonic disc of high quality. On the other hand, the lower recording level means that, since the groove cut is less deep, the groove is also narrower. And this makes possible a finer groove spacing, which in turn permits more playing time per record side.

If the stylus momentarily loses contact with the groove, as may happen on a heavily recorded passage, the 25-kc carrier frequency is lost temporarily, and the audible result is a moderate bass thump in the speaker. This problem can be overcome by incorporating a special oscillator in the preamplifier that continues the carrier frequency during the absence of contact between stylus and groove. This oscillator may be thought of as an electronic flywheel.

The systems described in this chapter are of interest since they indicate some of the numerous possible approaches in stereo techniques. However, none of these are in commercial use, since all record companies have adopted the Westrex system.

stereo on tape

S TEREO sound was first introduced to the public through the medium of tape. Toward the end of the 1940's, tape machines and prerecorded tapes intended for binaural reproduction were available. But as it became clear that earphones were a nuisance, attention turned to reproduction through speakers. Therefore, in recording, the microphones were spaced a number of feet apart in the manner of speakers rather than several inches apart in the manner of human ears. Thus, in the early 1950's, the pioneering audiophile had available to him stereo via speakers.

Yet stereo on tape did not show signs of making headway until some five years later. The delay was due to the slow emergence of relatively low-priced home machines with satisfactory electrical and mechanical performance and to the difficulties that had to be overcome in making high-quality tape duplicates at a reasonable price.

The earliest tape machines with mechanical and electrical characteristics satisfying high-fidelity requirements cost several hundreds of dollars, some much more. The frequency response, distortion, signal-to-noise ratio, wow and flutter, and speed accuracy of home machines left a good deal to be desired.

Frequency response flat within 2 db from about 30 cycles to at least 12,000 cycles, a signal-to-noise ratio in playback of at least 50 and preferably 55 db, harmonic distortion of no more than 1% or 2% on peaks, wow and flutter below 0.2% and speed accurate within 0.2%—these characterize a tape machine properly deserving the label of high fidelity. By 1956, the number of moderately-

priced tape machines within reasonable distance of these standards had become large enough to make it possible for stereo on
tape to progress rapidly. On the other hand, to this day there are
a substantial number of tape machines that claim high fidelity
yet fall considerably short of adequate performance.

Tape duplication

There is only one practical way of copying a tape conveying
audio information. It must be played from beginning to end, and
as this is done the signal is recorded onto the duplicate. This is
a much more protracted process than is used for disc recording,
where the major part of an hour of music may be stamped at
once upon a vinylite platter. To make tape duplication at all
economical, it was necessary to find means for making a number
of copies simultaneously and to reduce the copying time.

By 1956, the technology of tape duplication had reached the
point where a dozen copies could be made simultaneously from
a master tape, with all of them running at four or eight times
normal speed. Thus, in the case of a two-track stereo tape containing 32 minutes of music on a full reel, operating at 7.5 inches per
second, a dozen copies could be made in 4 or 8 minutes. The
problems of tape duplication do not merely involve speeding up
the copying process. Preservation of the quality of the master tape
is also a paramount consideration. Fig. 601 shows a successful
tape-duplicating machine which meets the requirements.

When the much less expensive stereo disc suddenly loomed over
the horizon, interest in tape slackened. However, the literature of
the day indicated that the interruption of progress was only
temporary. Stereo tape and the stereo disc each had its own role
to play, with the disc serving the portion of the market—probably
the larger portion—interested in price as much as quality, while
tape would serve those willing to pay for the utmost quality. In
other words, it was claimed that the general quality of tape would
be superior to that of discs, in the same manner as it used to be
claimed that tape would be the better medium for monophonic
reproduction. But all these foregoing statements describe only the
expectations of those in the industry and do not signify that tape
is always superior.

The slowdown in sales of stereo tapes and tape machines in
1958 was also caused by three new developments whose impact
was not immediately clear, causing audiophiles to wait for a
resolution of the situation before proceeding to invest their money.
These developments, which will be described later in detail, were:

1. Stereo tapes containing four tracks instead of two, with a consequent doubling of playing time on a given amount of tape, or a reduction in tape cost for a given playing time. Two of the tracks are reproduced when the tape is played in one direction, and the other two when the reels have been reversed and the tape is therefore played in the other direction.

2. The tape magazine, eliminating the need for threading reels, loading the tape past heads and guides, etc. Hence tape would be virtually as simple to handle as the phonograph disc.

3. High-quality tape recording at 3.75 ips instead of the 7 5-ips

Fig. 601. *The Dubbings tape duplicator can produce 12 tapes simultaneously.* (Courtesy Dubbings Sales Corp.)

speed hitherto considered the minimum for high fidelity. Again this makes possible either a doubling of playing time or a halving of cost.

Tape vs disc

It appears that tape is capable of providing higher fidelity than disc, although this is not the same thing as saying that the commercial prerecorded tapes live up to their potential by always surpassing the same music on disc. Poor tapes are to be found.

Based on a recording level that produces no more than about

1% harmonic distortion on peaks, which correspond to about 3% to 5% intermodulation distortion, a tape is inherently capable of producing a signal-to-noise ratio of about 65 db. This is very close to the dynamic range of a full orchestra, a large choral group and other massive sources of music; seldom does their dynamic range —the difference between loudest and quietest passages—exceed 70 db. More typically, the range is about 60 db. Hence tape can reproduce all the volume shadings of the original music. The typical disc is somewhat more limited in this respect having a dynamic range of about 50 db. If the attempt were made to reproduce the softest passages of, say, an orchestra at the same level relative to the loudest passages as in the original performance, then the softest passages would be below the noise produced by the record material—the softest passages would be inaudible. Accordingly, in making a phono recording, it is necessary to employ a considerable amount of compression; that is, bringing up the softest passages and attenuating the loudest so that the difference between them is within the compass of the phono disc.

Signal-to-noise ratio

It is far from a simple thing to realize the dynamic range of which tape is capable. The design and construction of the associated electronic apparatus must be precise and the user must take precautions to keep noise in the apparatus at a minimum. As noise produced by the tape machine increases, it obscures the quietest passages—thus limiting the dynamic range—and also interferes with pleasurable listening to the music as a whole. Even among expensive tape machines of semiprofessional and professional quality, seldom is a signal-to-noise ratio in excess of 55 db achieved in the electronic components. On rare occasions, a ratio as high as 60 db is attained, but only in the costliest of apparatus.

It is a good deal easier to achieve a satisfactory signal-to-noise ratio in the electronic apparatus—the preamplifier or control amplifier—used for reproduction of phonograph discs. Signal-to-noise ratios in excess of 55 db are quite common, reaching as high as 75 db in home equipment of moderate cost.

The greater difficulty in achieving a satisfactory signal-to-noise ratio (at least 55 db) with tape than disc is partly due to the smaller signal delivered by the tape head, which is typically about 2 or 3 millivolts maximum on peaks for an acceptable level of distortion. Higher signal output would require recording levels producing excessive distortion. Since phono playback cartridges produce substantially more output, noise in the electronic equipment is less likely to come up to the level of the signal.

The disadvantage of tape in the matter of signal-to-noise ratio also stems from the equalization required in playback. Both the tape head and the magnetic phono cartridge require bass boost. But the bass boost needed by the tape head is substantially more, resulting in greater hum amplification. Moreover, a magnetic phono cartridge requires treble cut, which can simultaneously reduce amplifier noise, whereas no such cut is employed in connection with a tape head. On the contrary, treble boost is often used to compensate for treble losses in the tape playback head. A piezoelectric (ceramic or crystal) phono pickup delivers a good deal more signal than a magnetic cartridge—on the order of 1 volt—and requires no bass boost, so that noise generated by the amplifier is still less likely to come up to the level of the audio signal produced by the cartridge.

At the tape speed of 7.5 ips, hitherto considered standard for high-fidelity home use, frequency response out to 15,000 cycles is quite practical. Response of this sort appears more difficult to achieve with a phono disc. Tape recording and playback is an electromagnetic process and does not entail mechanical oscillatory motion at rates up to 15,000 times per second. In the case of phono reproduction, however, the recording stylus and the playback stylus must vibrate at such rates, presenting physical problems. Moreover, with record use, the higher frequencies tend to disappear from the groove due to the forces developed by the rapidly moving stylus. All in all, tape appears to have an advantage over disc in the matter of high-frequency response. At the low end, however, neither medium appears to have a decided superiority.

With respect to mechanical motion, tape playback does not appear to be better than disc. Wow and flutter tend to be at least as great as for turntables of comparable quality; if anything, motion problems are more serious for tape apparatus. Accurate speed is easier to obtain on phonographs, many of which provide speed adjustments that permit absolute accuracy. There are as yet extremely few tape machines that permit the user to ascertain the degree of error in speed and to make the necessary correction readily.

Disc has had a decided advantage in convenience of operation. Compared with the simple procedure of placing a record on a turntable and either pushing a button for automatic start or manually lifting the tone arm and then placing the stylus on the record, putting a reel of tape on a machine, threading the tape past the heads and guiding devices, and fastening it to a takeup reel is much more complex. While the tape magazine will offer comparable operating ease, there will still be two advantages of disc to overcome: (1) permitting the user to locate the start of a passage partway on the disc; (2) enabling him to play several hours of music by placing a number of records on a changer.

In the matter of cost, disc thus far has had a very distinct advantage over tape, costing about one-half to one-third as much

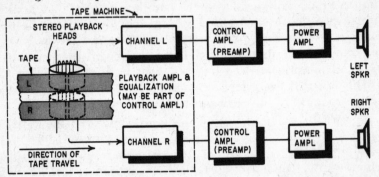

Fig. 602. *The fundamental elements of a stereo tape playback system.*

for the same playing time. However, the cost difference will be substantially reduced as four-track tapes designed to operate at 3.75 ips come into use.

Although initially more expensive, tape is potentially less expensive on a *per play* basis. With proper care it can be played thousands of times without significant loss of quality. Proper care means that the playback heads are periodically demagnetized to prevent addition of noise to the tape and erasure of high frequencies. It also means that the tape is kept away from extreme heat and magnetic fields.

There is some question as to whether the typical user will play a stereo tape enough times more than a stereo disc to realize this advantage. It has been claimed that with careful attention to such matters as tracking pressure, cleaning and destaticizing of the disc, etc., a stereo record can maintain close to its original quality for plays ranging from 50 to 300.[1] Others, however, have maintained that in a short while the stereo characteristics as well as the highest frequencies of the disc tend to disappear, even though the

[1] Joel Ehrlich, "How Compatible Are Stereo Discs?" *Audiocraft*, October, 1958.

record continues to sound clean. Altogether, it appears that stereo tapes do have a decided, practical advantage over stereo discs in terms of life.

Stereo tape systems

Fig. 602 shows the essentials of a stereo tape playback system. Assuming the tape moves from left to right, the signal of the left channel, L, is recorded on the upper portion (track) of the tape, while the R signal is recorded on the lower.

The magnetic patterns on each track correspond to the audio signals originally picked up by the stereo microphones. When the tape is played, separate heads, usually combined in one housing, scan each track and generate voltages corresponding to the magnetic patterns. The signal voltages produced by the heads are fed to a tape amplifier for amplification and equalization to produce a flat frequency response. The amplifier may or may not be part of the control amplifier of the audio system. Assuming the tape

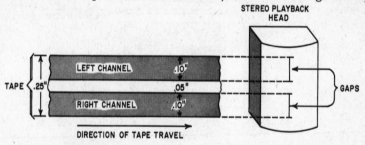

Fig. 603. *The tracks on a stereo tape are separated by a safety island to prevent crosstalk.*

amplifier is part of the tape machine, the signals are then fed, in the usual manner, to control amplifiers, power amplifiers and stereo speakers.

As shown in Fig. 603, each track is about 0.10 inch wide, with a "safety island" of about .05 inch between them to prevent the information on track L from being picked up by the right-channel playback head, and vice versa. Picking up the signal from the wrong channel is referred to as crosstalk. When mounting or adjusting the placement of heads, take care that the vertical positioning is such as to prevent this.

In-line vs staggered tapes

It is virtually universal practice to employ what is known as the in-line head (Fig. 604). It contains two sections, each equivalent to a separate head. The sections are mounted one directly above the other so that their gaps—the portion that picks up the signal from the tape—are in exact vertical alignment.

Yet until quite recently, at least as late as 1957, it was common practice to use the arrangement of Fig. 605, two distinct heads in what is termed the staggered-head arrangement. The heads were spaced about 1.25 inches apart. In a tape machine in which the tape moves from left to right, the channel L head would be at the left, its gap spanning the upper track, while the R head would be 1.25 inches to the right, spanning the lower track.

Prior to 1957, the staggered arrangement was used, which meant that most prerecorded stereo tapes sold were intended for playback

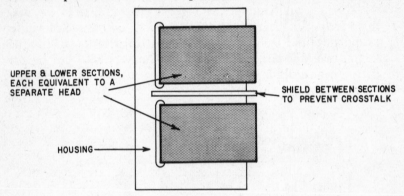

UPPER & LOWER SECTIONS, EACH EQUIVALENT TO A SEPARATE HEAD

SHIELD BETWEEN SECTIONS TO PREVENT CROSSTALK

HOUSING

Fig. 604. *The basic construction of an in-line stereo tape head.*

by staggered heads. Some of these tapes are still in existence, but cannot be played by an in-line head, unless one is willing to tolerate a distinct time lag between the two channels. Therefore some tape machines incorporate an extra playback head to permit the user to play either an in-line or a staggered-head stereo tape.

If in playback the heads for each channel have a different spacing than in recording, the phase relationship between the two stereo channels is altered. That is, the audio signals are at different relative portions of the cycle in playback than when they were picked up by the stereo microphones. A number of authorities feel that this change in phase relationship impairs, or at least alters, the stereo effect, and they place great emphasis upon maintaining the same spacing between heads (or rather their gaps) in playback as in recording. Some feel that it is necessary to maintain spacing accurate to .0001 inch. For this as well as other reasons, the in-line head was developed, with the two gaps in fixed relationship, one above the other.

To combine the equivalent of two heads into a housing no bigger than the space previously occupied by one head, to place their gaps in exact vertical alignment and to prevent the two sections from interfering with each other (crosstalk) was no small technological feat. Consequently, in-line heads were initially more expensive than two separate conventional heads designed to play only one track.

Use of an in-line head instead of staggered heads simplifies matters from the point of view of finding space on the tape transport to mount the heads. Moreover, it facilitates the process of

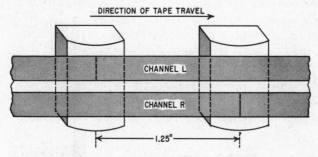

Fig. 605. *Staggered heads, once used for the playback of stereo tape, have been replaced by the in-line type.*

azimuth alignment. The gap of the playback head must be as nearly as possible at right angles to the long dimension of the

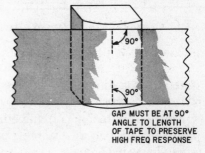

Fig. 606. *The gap in the playback head must be at right angles with the tape or a severe loss of high-frequency response occurs.*

tape, as shown in Fig. 606. A very slight deviation from a right angle will result in substantial loss of high frequencies. Finally, use of an in-line head simplifies problems of editing. If a staggered tape is to be cut and spliced, this must be done in diagonal fashion, more difficult to do with professional precision than making a right-angle cut.

Two-way systems

Ordinarily a monophonic tape is recorded with two tracks,

usually referred to as half-track recording because each track occupies nearly half the width of the tape (after allowing for the safety island). In a machine that moves the tape from left to right, the upper track of a monophonic tape is played back. When the tape has run out and the reels are reversed by the operator, thus turning the tape upside down, the other track becomes the upper one and can be played back to the starting position of the tape. This eliminates the necessity for rewinding, assuming the listener wishes to hear both tracks.

But a stereo tape monopolizes both tracks and therefore can be played only in one direction. This is referred to as a one-way tape. Obviously, rewinding is always necessary for such a tape. This can prove to be a decided inconvenience, particularly when playing long musical selections, such as operas, that occupy more than one reel.

Furthermore, a stereo tape that can be played only in one direction contains only half as much music as a monophonic tape that has programs both ways. Since the tape itself is a substantial factor

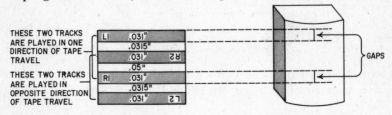

Fig. 607. *The Shure two-way stereo tape system increases playing time.*

in the cost of prerecorded tapes, this accounts to a considerable extent for the much greater cost of stereo tapes compared with stereo discs, a differential of about 2 to 1 or 3 to 1 when two-track stereo tapes operating at 7.5 ips are compared with stereo discs.

Aimed at reducing cost and eliminating the need for rewinding, proposals for two-way stereo tapes—also called four-track stereo tapes—have been made. Two such proposed systems differ in a slight but important respect. One basic system, illustrated in Fig. 607, was suggested by Shure Brothers, manufacturers of tape heads. In a tape traveling from left to right, tracks L1 and R1, respectively, provide the channel L and R stereo information. After the tape has been played in one direction and the reels reversed, tracks L2 and R2 provide the stereo signals.

Fig. 608 compares the space occupied by the tracks in the Shure system with the tracks on a conventional one-way stereo tape.

The four tracks fall within the same space occupied by the tracks on the one-way tape; the same safety island of .05 inch is maintained in the middle of the tape. Accordingly, a tape head designed to play four-track tapes (Fig. 607) can also play one-way stereo tapes. However, the shorter gaps of the four-track head would each cover only about one-third of the 0.10-inch tracks on a one-way tape. The result would be lower signal output from the four-track head than from a regular stereo head designed for two-track tape.

The narrower tracks in the two-way system are at a disadvantage relative to the signal-to-noise ratio. The wider the track,

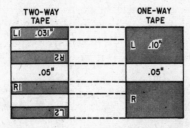

Fig. 608. *A comparison of the Shure system with a conventional stereo tape.*

the greater the magnetization on the tape and therefore the greater is the signal voltage produced by the playback head. And the greater the signal voltage, the higher is the ratio of the audio information to noise generated in the electronic components of the tape machine and in the following audio system. Reduction of the width of each track to about one-third of that in a one-way

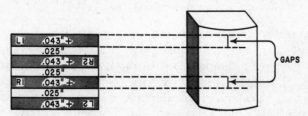

Fig. 609. *The RCA two-way stereo tape system uses wider recording tracks with narrower spacing between them than the Shure system.*

system results in an appreciable reduction in signal-to-noise ratio. Considering that tape machines must struggle hard to achieve a signal-to-noise ratio approaching 55 db, several db loss in that ratio due to narrower tracks can be ill afforded.

On the other hand, some of this loss in signal-to-noise ratio can be recouped by manufacturing playback heads with a greater number of coil turns. The more turns, the higher the output voltage of the head. But there are limits to this because the more turns, the greater the hum pickup—which reduces the signal-to-noise ratio—and the greater the loss of high frequencies due to capacitance between turns. Accordingly, more stringent and more expensive measures must be taken to shield the playback head from hum sources. And shorter leads must be used between the playback head and the following electronic components to keep capacitance across the head to a minimum and thereby preserve high-frequency response.

The tape consists essentially of a coating of finely dispersed particles of ferrous oxide in a material that binds them to a plastic base. The minute particles of magnetic oxide are spread out as homogeneously as possible, but it is difficult to achieve nearly

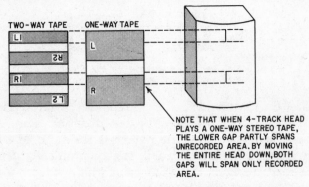

NOTE THAT WHEN 4-TRACK HEAD PLAYS A ONE-WAY STEREO TAPE, THE LOWER GAP PARTLY SPANS UNRECORDED AREA. BY MOVING THE ENTIRE HEAD DOWN, BOTH GAPS WILL SPAN ONLY RECORDED AREA.

Fig. 610. *Comparison of the RCA two-way system with a conventional tape.*

perfect results except at inordinate expense (high-quality tape for electronic computers costs the equivalent of about $50 to $100 for a 1,200-foot reel, compared with about $3 for a similar reel of audio tape). Irregularities in the tape coating cause noise and what is known as "dropouts," an absence or near-absence of recorded information. When a relatively wide portion of the tape is used for recording one track, the irregularities tend to average and to cancel. But when the track is quite narrow, there is less chance for the irregularities to average, so that they have a relatively greater effect, producing more noticeable pops, other noise and dropouts.

As a partial solution of the problems caused by the narrow tracks on a two-way stereo tape, RCA has brought forward a somewhat different version of four-track tape, as shown in Fig. 609. While the relative arrangement of tracks is the same as in Figs. 607 and 608, the spacing is different. In the RCA system, the tracks are nearly 50% wider than in the Shure method, with a resulting increase in signal output from the playback head. At the same time, the safety islands between tracks are smaller, and the middle island is no longer the same as in one-way stereo tape.

Fig. 610 compares the tracks on an RCA two-way stereo tape with those on a one-way stereo tape. If a four-track head is used to play a one-way tape, the lower gap of the in-line head will cover less recorded area than the upper gap. Hence, the lower section will have less signal output than the upper. To solve this problem, some tape machines incorporate a device that moves the four-track

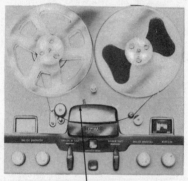

CONTROL FOR ONE-WAY STEREO TAPES

Fig. 611. *A stereo tape machine with provision for moving the heads up to play two-way tapes and down to play conventional stereo or monophonic tapes.* (Courtesy Ampex Corp.)

head slightly downward for playing one-way stereo tapes. Such a machine is shown in Fig. 611.

There is always the possibility that the problems raised by four-track stereo tapes will be partly solved by improvements in the tape itself. In the past, there have been improvements in the amount of signal the tape can accept before significant distortion is caused, and in noise and dropouts. Conceivably, the future may witness similar advances, although not to the same degree. On the other hand, refinements in heads and in the electronics of the amplifiers following them are also likely to play a part in recouping the signal-to-noise ratio that is lost through the use of narrower tracks.

The tape magazine

One obstacle to large-scale acceptance of tape as a commercial medium for reproduction of sound in the home has been the relatively cumbersome process of playing a tape, compared with

Fig. 612. *The RCA magazine for use with tapes recorded by their method contains up to 1 hour of music.*

the simplicity of playing a phonograph record. To simplify tape playback, as well as to reduce the cost of prerecorded tape, the tape magazine was introduced by RCA. As shown in Fig. 612, the

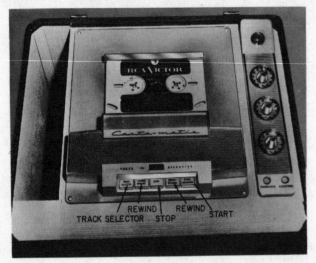

Fig. 613. *The RCA tape magazine in place on a special tape machine.*

tape is enclosed in a plastic container that measures 7 inches long, 5 inches wide and only ½ inch deep. The container is placed on a special tape machine designed for this purpose, and the tape engages the heads and driving mechanism, as shown in Fig. 613. The reels in the plastic container are held securely by an automatic brake that is released when the magazine is properly positioned on the tape machine. The tape begins to play when a button is pushed.

While convenience is achieved through the magazine loading technique, cost is reduced by the following two expedients: (1) by recording four tracks on the tape in the manner previously discussed; (2) by operating the tape at 3.75 instead of 7.5 ips, heretofore considered the minimum speed for high-fidelity performance. Altogether, these steps are calculated to make up to 60 minutes of music available in a magazine at a cost less than half of present two-way stereo tapes operating at 7.5 ips.

The increase in playing time achieved through the transition

Fig. 614. *The full reel holds conventional stereo tape which will produce music for the same length of time as the smaller length of four-track tape.*

from stereo one-way tape operating at 7.5 ips to stereo two-way tape operating at 7.5 or 3.75 ips may be shown for a 600-foot reel of tape:

Mode of Operation	Playing Time
One-way, 7.5 ips	16 minutes
Two-way, 7.5 ips	32 minutes
Two-way, 3.75 ips	64 minutes

Conversely, for a given playing time, two-way 3.75-ips operation can achieve a substantial saving in tape. This is graphically demonstrated in Fig. 614. At the right is shown the amount of tape required to play about ½ hour of music on one-way stereo tape at 7.5 ips—about 1,200 feet. At the left is shown the amount of tape required when operating on a two-way 3.75-ips basis—about 300 feet. The cost of a prerecorded tape, of course, does not go down as fast as the reduction in tape required for a given playing time.

The convenience value of the tape magazine would be lost unless means were provided for automatically stopping the tape before it runs out. This is done by the special tape player designed to accommodate the magazine. Moreover, some models of this tape player automatically reverse the tape after it has come to the end of its run. To do this, it is necessary to incorporate another playback head in the machine or else provide some means for shifting the position of the playback head to scan the correct tracks.

One of the problems raised by the attempt to use the 3.75-ips speed for high-fidelity purposes is that of wow and flutter, or slow or rapid fluctuations in speed. A tape transport operating at

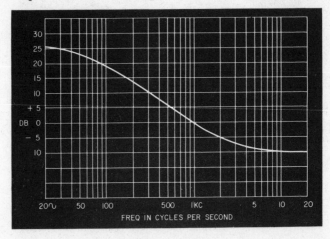

Fig. 615. *NARTB playback equalization for a 7.5-ips tape.*

high speed has greater mechanical inertia and therefore less susceptibility to speed fluctuations than one operating at low speed. At a speed as low as 3.75 ips, it requires a high order of craftsmanship to keep wow and flutter below 0.25%.

Another, and probably the most serious, problem raised by the 3.75-ips speed is that of adequate frequency response at the high end.

Frequency response

Commercial stereo tapes designed to operate at 7.5 ips are generally recorded in a manner that requires a substantial amount of bass boost in playback. The amount of equalization necessary is shown in Fig. 615; this is referred to as NARTB equalization. For tapes operating at 3.75 ips, the playback equalization is frequently that of Fig. 616. Failure to provide correct equalization at either speed will result in insufficient or excessive bass or treble. Taking 7.5-ips tape as an example, it is not uncommon to find

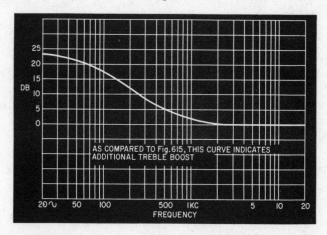

Fig. 616. *Playback equalization for a 3.75 ips tape.*

tape machines or control-amplifiers (where the signal from the tape head is fed directly into the control amplifier for equalization) that provide substantially smaller amounts of bass boost than required. The result is inadequate bass and excessive treble.

Adequate treble response depends upon: (1) Tape speed—the higher the speed, the higher is the frequency response of which the system is capable. (2) The tape—there is some variation among brands and types of tape as to their high-frequency capabilities. (3) Bias current (high-frequency current applied to the recording head simultaneously with the audio signal to reduce distortion and increase the amount of signal recorded on the tape—the greater the bias current, the poorer is the high-frequency response. (4) The width of the gap in the playback head—the narrower the gap, the better is the treble response. (5) Treble emphasis in recording to overcome treble losses that take place in the process of impressing a signal on the tape.

The attempt to use 3.75 ips for high-fidelity purposes raises questions in regard to all of these factors:

1. Tape speed: If response at 7.5 ips is relatively flat to 15,000 cycles, then changing to the 3.75-ips speed without changing anything else will result in response being good to only 7,500 cycles. However, flat response to at least 10,000 or 12,000 cycles is considered a minimum requirement for high fidelity.

2. The tape: While some improvement in tape may occur to assist in extension of the treble range at 3.75 ips, no major breakthrough is expected.

3. Bias current: It may well be that less bias current will have to be employed for 3.75-ips tapes than is presently used for 7.5 ips to reduce treble-attenuating effects. The penalty, however, is greater distortion, because as bias is decreased distortion goes up. A severe rise in distortion can be avoided, however, by recording at lower levels; distortion goes up or down as recording level goes up or down. But a lower recording level means a lower signal-to-noise ratio. Altogether, less bias may entail either higher distortion or a lower signal-to-noise ratio or a combination of the two. (The reduction in recorded signal may be offset by more efficient playback heads that produce more signal for a given amount of magnetization on the tape.)

4. Gap width: A playback head with a gap width of .00025 inch has been considered adequate for 7.5-ips recording, resulting in a loss of only about 4 or 5 db at 15,000 cycles, which can easily be made up (if considered necessary) by treble boost. But if used for 3.75 ips, such a head would result in extremely great losses beyond 10,000 cycles. However, playback heads have recently been developed having gaps of only .00009 inch, which result in very little loss out to 15,000 cycles. On the other hand, all other things being equal, a head with a very narrow gap tends to have less signal output than one with a wider gap, resulting in a reduced signal-to-noise ratio.

5. Recording treble boost: In recording 7.5-ips tapes, very substantial amounts of treble boost—in excess of 20 db—are employed in recording to permit a response extending to about 15,000 cycles. Boost much greater than 20 db will result in excessive distortion being recorded on the tape. Yet in recording at 3.75 ips, if response is to extend this high, treble boost considerably greater than 20 db would be required. To avoid excessive distortion, it is necessary to record at a somewhat lower level at 3.75 ips than at 7.5 ips, which means a lower signal-to-noise ratio.

All in all, 3.75-ips tapes present very definite problems if they are to satisfy high-fidelity dictates. Nevertheless, it is to be expected that technological improvements will bring about satisfactory solutions, although some of these may be several years distant.

Crosstalk

Crosstalk between channels is much less of a problem for stereo tape than disc, with 40 db or more of isolation between channels being obtained for tape. The principal source of crosstalk is in the in-line head, where the closely adjacent sections result in mutual coupling of the signal between sections. That is, each section, through magnetic induction, tends to pick up some of the signal present in the other.

Although slight crosstalk is not objectionable when playing stereo tapes, it presents a problem when one section of an in-line head is used to play a half-track monophonic tape. If the upper section of the in-line head is used to play the upper track of a

Fig. 617. *A stereo tape transport designed for use with external amplification facilities.* (Courtesy Telectrosonic Corp.)

monophonic tape, the unused lower section will nevertheless pick up signal from the lower track; and some of the lower-track signal will be inductively transferred to the upper section of the head. Presence of the signal from the lower track, which is completely unrelated to the upper track on a monophonic tape (moreover, the lower track is operating in the wrong direction), can be disturbing even in slight amounts, particularly during quiet

127

passages on the upper track. The audiophile who wishes to play monophonic as well as stereo tapes is well advised to pay careful attention to the crosstalk characteristics of the in-line head. Crosstalk isolation of at least 50 db appears necessary for satisfactory use of such a head.

The problem of crosstalk in the head is less for an in-line head designed for two-way (four-track) operation than for one-way (two-track) operation. In Figs. 607 and 609, the distance between the gaps is greater for two-way heads. In the Shure system, the distance between gaps is 0.1125 inch and in the RCA system it is

Fig. 618. *Two types of external tape-amplifiers: (above) this unit is designed for playback only; (below) a more complex unit which contains facilities for record and playback. When used for stereo the units shown are used in pairs.* (Courtesy Telectrosonic Corp.)

.093 inch, compared with a distance of .05 inch for one-way heads. The greater the distance between the gaps of an in-line head, the greater the opportunity for shielding each section from the other to reduce crosstalk.

Stereo tape installations

The individual seeking stereo sound through tape will find that the "tape machine" he buys may be any one of a number of things in terms of the functions it performs. It may range from something as simple as a transport mechanism that only moves the tape past the heads, without any following electronic components, to something in the way of a complete audio system, including speakers. Following are the basic variations in the "package" that the audiophile may purchase from manufacturers of tape machines.

1. A tape transport mechanism, such as shown in Fig. 617. The signal from the stereo playback head is fed directly to the control amplifiers of the audio system. It is common practice today for control amplifiers to incorporate the equalization and extra amplification required to accept the signal from a tape head and produce flat response at a sufficient voltage level to drive a power amplifier. However, a caution is in order. The cable between the heads and

Fig. 619. *This stereo tape system includes a tape transport, external playback and record amplifiers and an integrated stereo amplifier and preamplifier.* (Courtesy Telectrosonic Corp.)

the control amplifiers must be kept short to minimize loss of high frequencies.

2. A unit that consists of a tape transport together with playback components or one may acquire the playback components (see

Fig. 618) separately. These units provide the equalization and amplification necessary to convert the signal from the tape head into a flat signal at high enough voltage to drive a control amplifier or power amplifier.

3. A tape transport together with components not only for playback but also for recording, so that the audiophile can make his own tapes. Sometimes there are record facilities for only one channel, so that one is confined to monophonic recording. Sometimes there are facilities for both channels, so one can record stereo. Some of the units just described come with either one or two microphones, and some come with none.

4. A package containing not only playback and record components but also power amplifiers and speakers. Sometimes there is just one power amplifier and one speaker, sometimes two power amplifiers and two speakers (one or both speakers outside the housing of the tape machine), sometimes two power amplifiers and one speaker. To the extent that there is not a full complement of two power amplifiers and two speakers, the user is expected to fill in. Fig. 619 shows a complete stereo tape system.

stereo microphone techniques

A RUDIMENTARY acquaintance with the techniques and problems of setting up microphones for stereo recording is of value to the audiophile in several ways. It can provide clues as to the manner in which he should set up his speakers, for certain microphone techniques presume a correspondence between speaker and microphone placement. It can be of direct assistance in the event he acquires a stereo tape recorder and makes recordings in his home, school, church or similar place.

Stereo microphone techniques cannot follow hard and fast rules. Every situation has its special characteristics and therefore its own specific solution to the problem. Optimum microphone placement depends upon the nature of the sound source, the characteristics of the performance site, the types of microphones used, and even on the characteristics of the reproduction site. Thus, best results are to be had through experimentation rather than slavish adherence to a set of rules. On the other hand there are some guiding principles, reflected in several basic methods of recording stereo.

Binaural recording

Stereo reproduction, via tape, was originally meant to be heard through earphones, the left channel through the left earphone and the right channel through the other earphone. The original technique of microphone placement was to use two microphones about 8 inches apart and to separate them by a partition of a size and shape similar to the head, as illustrated in Fig. 701. In effect, the two microphones took the place of the listener's ears at the original performance, and through the medium of tape the sound that reached each microphone was preserved until it could reach the listener (Fig. 702).

For practical recording, it is rather inconvenient to mount microphones as the ears of a dummy head. A practical means of

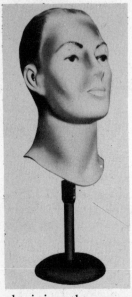

Fig. 701. *In binaural recording, the microphones are separated by the width of the human head. Conceivably a dummy head with microphones inserted in the position of the ears could be used.* (Courtesy Amplifier Corp. of America.)

obtaining the same separation is illustrated in Fig. 703 which shows a stand designed to hold two microphones with a rectangular partition between them.

The time-intensity technique

When it became obvious that the public did not take well to binaural reproduction, and that stereo, to be a commercial success, would have to reach the listener through speakers instead of ear-

Fig. 702. *The essential elements of a binaural system.*

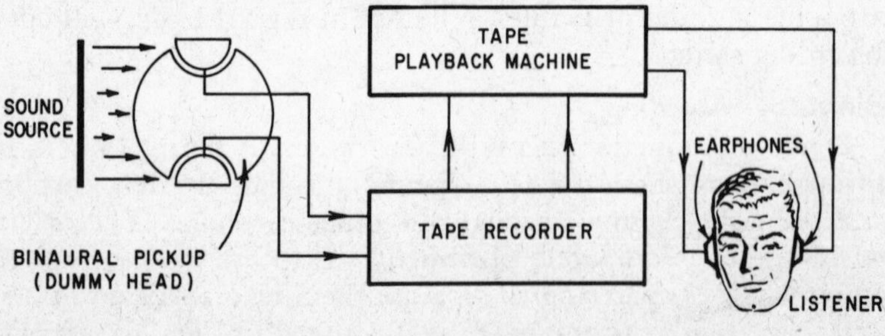

SOUND SOURCE

TAPE PLAYBACK MACHINE

EARPHONES

BINAURAL PICKUP (DUMMY HEAD)

TAPE RECORDER

LISTENER

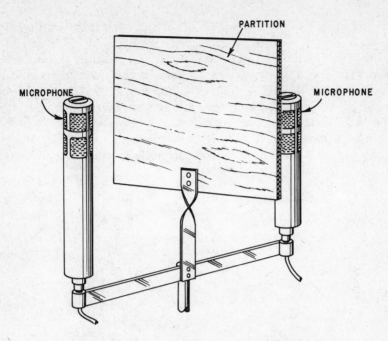

Fig. 703. *A practical setup for binaural recording.*

phones, the microphones were separated by a matter of feet, as illustrated in Fig. 704, instead of inches. Since the effect of such spacing is usually to produce a significant difference both in arrival

Fig. 704. *Microphone placement used in time-
intensity recording.*

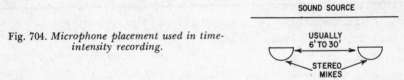

time and intensity of the sound at each microphone, it can be referred to as time-intensity recording.

An early form of the time-intensity method of deploying the microphones has been referred to as classical recording, where the distance between the microphones is supposed to be the same as the distance between the speakers at the reproduction site. This is an application of the curtain of sound principle, discussed in Chapter 1, where each of a number of microphone-speaker pairs is supposed to cover a portion of the sound in the lateral dimension. For two-channel stereo, however, there would be only two microphone-speaker links between the original sound source and the listener.

Classical recording has rather obvious limitations. Whereas a spacing of, say, eight feet would be adequate to span the breadth of such sound sources as a chamber group, concert artist and piano accompaniment, small chorus, etc., it would be quite inadequate for a symphony orchestra. Here, if the classical technique were to be followed, a spacing of as much 30 feet would be required between the microphones and speakers alike. But few homes could accommodate such a spacing between speakers. Moreover, even for sound sources where a microphone spacing of, say, eight feet is sufficient, it is difficult to presume that all stereo

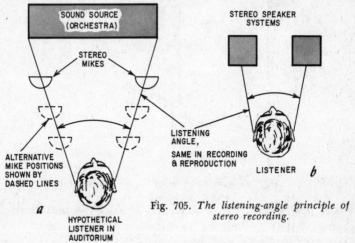

Fig. 705. *The listening-angle principle of stereo recording.*

speakers will be exactly eight feet apart, thereby maintaining the microphone-speaker pair concept. Hence the classical technique is difficult to apply in a strict sense.

In a loose sense, however, the classical recording *principle* is widely used, namely spacing microphones along the sound source to capture the lateral dimension of the sound. Accordingly, time-intensity recording has resulted in microphone spacing varying from about six to as much as thirty feet, so as to impress the listener with a sharp differentiation between the sound on the left and the sound on the right. While a spatial effect was indeed achieved by these forms of time-intensity recording, the results were not always realistic. If anything, the left–right differentiation was overdone, and after the first astonished reaction the discriminating listener soon found the character of the sound to be unnatural and disturbing.

Haphazard spacing of microphones eventually gave way to more logical procedures designed to maintain left–right orientation within realistic limits and at the same time achieve a fusion of the music as a whole. Accordingly, there has been a trend toward acceptance of the "listening-angle principle," which postulates a systematic relationship between microphones, speakers and listener.

This principle is based upon a standard angle, between 30° and 45°, that would be formed by a hypothetical listener at the original performance and the approximate extremes of the music source.

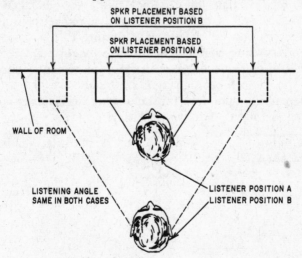

Fig. 706. *The placement of stereo speakers in accordance with the listening-angle principle and the distance of the listener from the speakers.*

The stereo microphones are mounted on the sides of the angle formed by the hypothetical listener and the source, as illustrated in Fig. 705-a. It is intended that in reproduction the two speakers shall be spaced to form about the same angle between the listener and the speakers (Fig. 705-b).

Fig. 705-a shows various positions in which the pair of stereo microphones can be placed, either closer to or farther from the source, yet always on the sides of the angle. If they are brought very close to the source and therefore are spaced a substantial distance apart due to the spread of the angle, there will be a strong differentiation between left and right but at the risk of losing much of the music issuing from the center of the source (in part this depends upon the coverage—polar characteristics—of the microphone used). If the microphones are too far up front, they will pick up relatively little indirect (reverberated) sound. The stereo requirement of spaciousness, achieved through a suitable ratio of indirect to direct sound pickup, may be sacrificed in exchange for directional effect.

If the stereo microphones are placed too far back, there will be less distinction between sound on the left and sound on the right, and reverberated sound will be given undue weight, causing the music to lose clarity and definition. Between extreme positions there is an intermediate one that achieves a good balance among the various factors that make a successful stereo recording; directionality, reverberation, clarity, etc. Finding this position is the task of the recording engineer or of the amateur recordist.

Fig. 705-b shows one of many speaker placements that would maintain the same listening angle as was used at the recording session. Depending upon how far the listener sits from the speakers, the spacing between them will be narrower or wider. This is

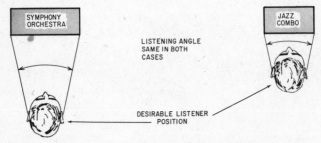

Fig. 707. *Variation of listening position with type of sound source, permitting same listening angle for sources of different width.*

illustrated in Fig. 706, which shows two speaker placements. The spacing between speakers increases as the listener's distance from them increases, maintaining the same angle.

The listening-angle principle does not confine the audiophile to an exact point in the room. Rather, he is free to move about, as he would in selecting a seat in the concert hall. But it does provide a basis for spacing the speakers, and it is probably true that the closer one sits to that point in the room which corresponds to the listening angle, the greater the stereo effect.

Initially it might seem as though the listening angle would be wider for a music source spread over a considerable space, as in the case of an orchestra, than for a source occupying a narrow area, such as a jazz combination. One might expect that the speakers in the home would have to be spaced more widely to reproduce the orchestra than the jazz combo. However, as illustrated in Fig.

707, one would sit much closer to a jazz combo at the actual performance than to a symphony orchestra. Therefore, the angle formed by the listener and the jazz combo tends to be about the same as the angle formed by the listener and the symphony orchestra. So, provided the listening angle is maintained, the same speaker arrangement can be employed to reproduce the narrow source as well as the wide one.

When recording large groups in accordance with the listening angle principle or other variations of the time-intensity technique,

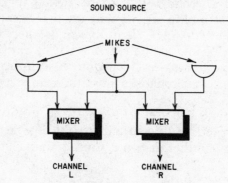

Fig. 708. *The use of three microphones for stereo recording.*

there may be a considerable distance between microphones, with a resulting tendency to lose some of the sound in the center. It is frequent practice to employ a central microphone (Fig. 708).

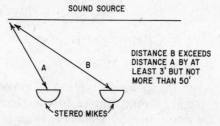

Fig. 709. *The spacing of stereo microphones to achieve a difference in arrival time.*

The signal produced by it is mixed with (added to) that of the left and right microphones. Professional recordists sometimes employ three-channel tape machines, so that the mixing can be done after the original performance, allowing the engineers to experiment with the amount of center-channel signal needed for optimum results. However, three-channel tape machines are quite costly and therefore unavailable to the amateur recordist, who must still do his mixing at the microphone stage.

Time-intensity recording causes a sound from the left to reach the right microphone a small interval after it reaches the left microphone. Attention must be paid to this interval for it to be significant, that is, to produce a stereo sensation based on time differences in the same sound issuing from the stereo speakers. According to expert opinion, the interval between arrival times at the stereo microphones should be at least 3 milliseconds (three thousandths of a second). Since sound travels slightly more than 1,000 feet per second in air, we may say that it travels roughly 1 foot per millisecond. And 3 milliseconds therefore represents about 3 feet. If sound at the extreme left or extreme right is to create a stereo effect based upon difference in arrival time, the path length to the microphones must differ by at least 3 feet (Fig. 709).

When the time delay exceeds about 50 milliseconds the ear begins to interpret the difference in arrival time, not as a sensation of direction, but rather as two distinct sounds. Therefore, when

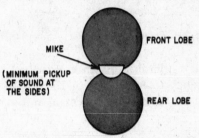

Fig. 710. *Figure-8 pickup pattern of microphone used for intensity-difference recording.*

recording in a large space, for example the average auditorium, the path length from a sound source to the stereo microphones must *not* differ by more than 50 feet. However, it is possible that in a very large auditorium and with a music source spread over a wide stage, path lengths to the microphones can differ as much as 50 feet and more.

Intensity-difference technique

While classical recording relies upon differences both in amplitude and arrival time at each microphone, the intensity-difference technique, quite popular in Europe, relies essentially upon differences in signal amplitude. The microphone setup is essentially similar to that for binaural recording, shown in Fig. 703. However, the microphones employed for intensity-difference recording have a different polar characteristic. They are most sensitive over an area corresponding to a figure 8, as shown in Fig. 710. That is, each microphone picks up sound to the front (front lobe) and to the rear (rear lobe), but picks up very little sound at either side.

For intensity-difference recording, the microphones are oriented (Fig. 711-a) so that the front lobe of one points toward the right of the sound source, and the front lobe of the other toward its left. Each front lobe also covers the center to some extent, so that the sound in the center is picked up. Since they are closely

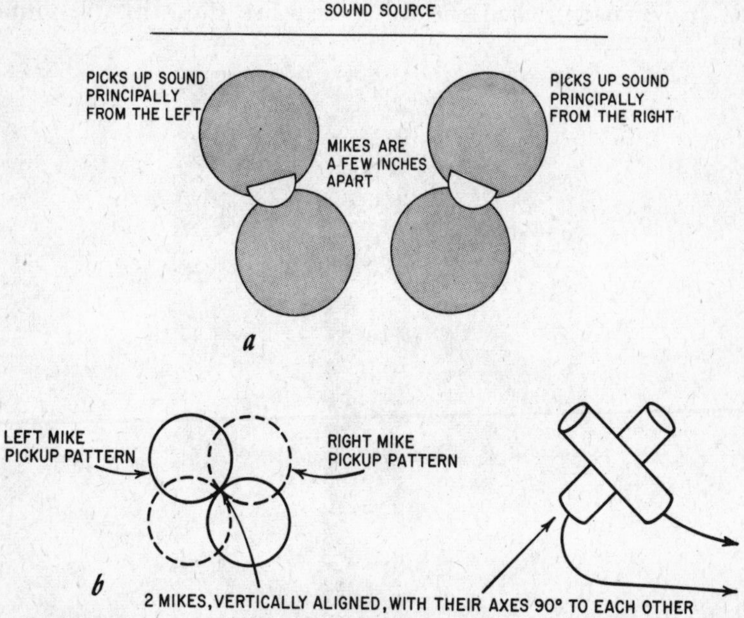

Fig. 711. *Use of two microphones with figure 8 patterns for intensity-difference recording (above). Stereosonic recording (below). This is a form of intensity-difference recording.*

spaced, the predominant difference in the signals arriving at each microphone is one of amplitude. Use of a partition between them increases the intensity difference. One manufacturer of equipment for such an arrangement claims that the amplitude difference is as if two conventional omnidirectional microphones (equally sensitive in all directions) were placed 10 feet apart.

At the higher frequencies, microphone spacing of several inches results in a considerable phase difference between the signals.

Assume the microphone spacing is 6 inches. At low frequencies, a wavelength of 1 cycle is a good deal more than 6 inches (for example, a wavelength of 100 cycles is about 10 feet), so that there cannot be much difference in phase (portion of the cycle at a given instant) at the two microphones. At high frequencies, however, a wavelength is short enough so that over a distance of 6 inches there can be an appreciable difference in phase. When the microphones are 6 inches apart, the phase differences can become significant at frequencies above 1,000 cycles or so (the wavelength of 1,000 cycles is about 12 inches). However, it is uncertain to what extent phase differences play a part in the stereo effect, particularly when the differences are those in the sound

Fig. 712. *The Neumann SM-2 microphone used for mid-side recording.*

issuing from each speaker and not necessarily in the sound arriving at each ear.

A specific form of intensity difference recording, known as Stereosonic recording, places the two microphones at 45° to each other and in the same vertical plane, as illustrated in Fig. 711-b. In this case the phase differences between microphones tend to be negligible.

Mid-side recording

A technique highly favored in Europe and likely to gain increasing acceptance in this country in view of its well-received results is the so-called mid-side recording technique, employing a specially designed microphone, the Neumann SM-2, sold in the United States under the name of Telefunken.

The unit, (Fig. 712) contains two capacitor microphones in one housing. The polar characteristic of each can be varied by voltages fed to them from a power supply. The mid-microphone is oriented toward the sound source and its polar characteristic is controlled by the power supply to assume a cardioid (heart-shaped) pattern (Fig. 713). The side microphone has its polar character-

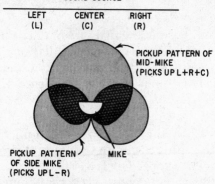

Fig. 713. *Pickup patterns of the elements of the SM-2 microphone.*

istic shaped into a figure 8 (as shown in Fig. 711) which is oriented parallel to the sound source (Fig. 713).

The mid-microphone is oriented by pointing it at the source; thus in the photo of Fig. 712, when the diamond-shaped label points at the source so does the lower microphone element. Sound reaches this element through the lower grille. By inserting a coin in the slit at the top (see photo), the upper element may be turned, thereby placing the upper microphone element parallel to the source. In this case, the sound reaches the element through the upper grilles at the left and right of the microphone housing.

The mid-microphone is oriented and its polar characteristic shaped to pick up all the sound, namely L + R + C, with L representing the left, R the right and C the center.

The side microphone picks up sound primarily from the left and right sides, or L and R. However, the signal it produces is not L + R but L — R. The side microphone has but one transducing element, which converts sound waves into an electrical signal. Obviously, this one element cannot move two ways at once. It will move in the same direction for a signal from the left as one

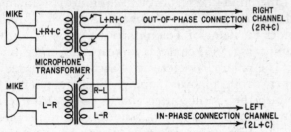

Fig. 714. *Combining the signals from the elements of the mid-side microphone to produce left- and right-channel information.*

from the right, only if these signals are of opposite phase. In other words, the element will move, say, from left to right if the sound from the left is positive in phase (pushing) while the sound from the right is negative in phase (pulling). Hence, the net motion of the transducing element and the electrical signal produced by the side microphone is L — R rather than L + R.

Fig. 714 shows how the signals from each microphone are combined, employing special windings on output transformers which are part of the microphone. The L — R and the L + R + C signals are connected in series in phase, therefore producing 2L + C. The L — R signal is taken out of phase by another winding, thus becoming R — L, which is combined in series with the L + R + C signal to produce 2R + C. In aggregate, one output channel contains information primarily from the left, while the other output channel contains information mostly from the right.

At the same time, both channels contain information representing the center of the sound source. This eliminates the problem of correctly placing a center microphone and of mixing its output with that of the left and right channels.

The mid-side microphone technique is advantageous in connection with stereophonic broadcasts by FM multiplex, using the difference-frequency principle. It was explained in Chapter 3 that with this method of broadcasting the main carrier contains all the sound information (L + R + C), while the stereo information, or L − R, is transmitted by the subcarrier. Thus, the owner of a conventional FM tuner, which detects only the main carrier, would receive all the audio information. The owner of a multiplex FM receiver would, in addition, receive the L − R signal. By combining L − R with L + R + C and then combining R − L with L + R + C, the multiplex receiving equipment thereby produces left-channel and right-channel signals. Use of a mid-side microphone eliminates the need on the part of the broadcast station for adding and subtracting the left and right signals. The L + R + C signal can be obtained directly from one element of the microphone, and the L − R signal can be obtained directly from the other element.

The SM-2 microphone has a price tag which places it out of reach of most amateurs. However, it is quite possible that the mid-side technique may become available through moderately-priced electronic mixers, which will enable one to use relatively

SOUND SOURCE

STEREO MIKES

Fig. 715. *Placement of the microphone for longitudinal stereo recording.*

low-priced microphones, one with a cardioid pattern and the other with a figure 8 pattern; the mixer would then combine the signals of the two microphones in proper fashion.

Longitudinal recording

In the course of the many experiments that have been conducted with respect to microphone placement, one of the techniques inevitably tried has been that of placing the microphones longitudinally (Fig. 715).

The contributions of longitudinal recording to the stereo effect are two: (1) There are differences in arrival time at each microphone. The spacing should be such as not to produce a delay of more than 50 milliseconds, which means a distance of not more than 50 feet between microphones (ample margin except in the largest halls). (2) There are differences in the ratio of direct to reverberated sound picked up by each microphone. The rear microphone will have a greater proportion of reverberated sound and therefore will tend more to the illusion of a large hall.

The difference in character of sound issuing from each speaker, resulting from the different amounts of reverberated sound picked up by each microphone, may be disturbing. One solution would be to channel the sound of the front microphone to a center speaker and the sound of the rear microphone to speakers at the right and left. Another possibility is to employ three microphones, two as in classical recording and the third as in longitudinal recording—that is, farther from the source (Fig. 716)—and then to mix the signal of the third microphone with the signals of the left and right microphones.

Matching microphones

Optimum performance requires that the microphones employed for stereo recording must be matched in several senses. One is in terms of frequency response. If the microphones have different sensitivities at various frequencies, the result may well be to cause the sound apparently to wander from left to right or right

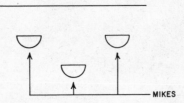

Fig. 716. *Microphone placement for combining longitudinal and classical recording.*

to left in reproduction, depending upon the dominant frequency at a given instant.

Matching is also important in terms of polar characteristics. If one microphone has a different coverage pattern than the other in classical or intensity-difference recording, sounds at left center may instead appear at center or right center, for example. Or there may be inadequate reproduction of sounds at left center, center or right center.

Third, matching is required in terms of overall sensitivity. Use of a highly sensitive microphone with one of low sensitivity leads to problems of balancing channels.

All told, to obtain microphones that maintain the same frequency response characteristic from unit to unit, the same polar characteristics and equal sensitivities, it is necessary to use more expensive units. On the other hand, for amateur recording, it is quite possible to learn to make the necessary compensations when working with microphones of moderate quality. To an extent,

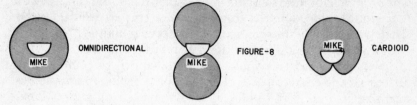

Fig. 717. *The three basic polar characteristics of microphones.*

experimentation can take the place of quality of apparatus, making it possible, after all, to obtain high-quality results with moderate-cost equipment.

Polar characteristics

The three basic polar characteristics of various types of microphones have already been discussed. But it is well to review what they are and the contributions of each.

Fig. 717 compares the three polar characteristics: omnidirectional, cardioid and figure 8. The omnidirectional and cardioid are probably best suited for classical recording, where the micro-

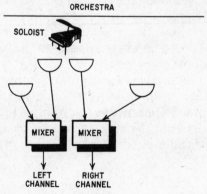

Fig. 718. *Using two pairs of microphones for stereo recording.*

phones are a substantial distance apart. Both types have a broad range of coverage and tend to pick up sound in the center to a better degree under conditions of wide separation than will the figure 8 microphone. The omnidirectional microphone will pick up much more of the sound at the rear than will the cardioid, thus increasing the ratio of indirect to direct sound and enhancing the effect of spaciousness. The cardioid, to achieve a comparable sensation of spaciousness, would have to be moved to a more distant location from the source. On the other hand, the cardioid, by concentrating on sound in front, provides greater definition and clarity and possibly freedom from extraneous sounds.

Of course, it is possible to use different types of microphones, in pairs, connected in parallel to each channel, to combine the desired pickup characteristics. For example, cardioid microphones might be used up front to pick up a soloist, while omnidirectional ones might be used at a greater distance to pick up the rest of a musical aggregation (with a substantial ratio of indirect to direct sound), as illustrated in Fig. 718.

Phasing

A problem that exists throughout stereo reproduction is to maintain proper phasing between channels, and this is just as true for microphones as for any other stage in the stereo chain. If the recordist employs different microphones for stereo, the problem of phasing may well come up. That is, if both microphones pick up the same sound, one may be delivering a positive signal when the other is delivering a negative signal, and vice versa. Proper phase can be established by experiment. If the microphones are fed into a stereo tape recorder, the same sound may be picked up by placing the two microphones close together, and then feeding the output of the tape machine into the stereo system. If the sound from the two speakers appears to come from a point approximately halfway between them, phasing is correct. It is assumed that the two speakers have previously been phased with respect to each other on the basis of a commercial stereo tape or stereo disc. If the sound appears to come from an indefinite region, the phasing is incorrect at the source—the microphones. It is then necessary to reverse the leads coming from one of the microphones.

amplifiers for stereo

C ONTROL over the various stereo functions lies in the control
amplifier rather than the power amplifier. Hence our concern
is with stereo units in the form of a control amplifier or an
integrated amplifier (combination control and power amplifier).
All references to an amplifier are to a unit containing control
facilities, unless specifically stated otherwise.[1]

A stereo amplifier is a good deal more than merely two of
everything. In addition to performing the usual functions of a
monophonic unit, it must serve two other objectives: (1) coordinating conventional functions of the two channels; (2) performing
functions unique to stereo and not found in monophonic
reproduction.

Because the stereo amplifier is so new, there is considerable
variation among manufactured units. The differences are substantially greater than among monophonic ones with respect to
functions performed and the manner in which they are performed.
This tends to be puzzling to the would-be purchaser, for not only
does he have cost and quality to think about but he must decide
among the varying combinations of features offered.

The different approaches employed by manufacturers permits
an evaluation in the field of alternative methods of coping with
the special problems raised by stereo—problems involving control
of gain, control of frequency response and loudness, balance

---

[1] Sometimes the control facilities are combined with an FM tuner or an FM–AM
tuner or a dual FM and AM tuner for stereo use. The discussion applies to such
equipment.

between channels, phasing, provision of a phantom channel, combination of channels, etc. The stereo amplifier appears to be repeating the history of the mono amplifier: it required a number of years to mature to its present form and establish the

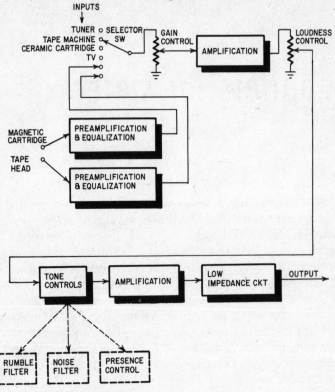

Fig. 801. *The essential functions of a conventional monophonic control amplifier are numerous and varied. Additional functions sometimes included are shown in dashed lines.*

nature of the controls required. Today monophonic amplifiers, while maintaining their individuality, have strong family resemblances. Similarly, experience will point the way to the best methods of meeting the specific problems raised by stereo, so that the differences among stereo amplifiers will be less than they are today.

To provide a basis for discussing a stereo control amplifier, it is advisable first to consider the operation of a monophonic unit.

Functions of a mono control amplifier

Fig. 801 indicates the essential functions of a conventional control unit. In the case of a signal from a magnetic phono pickup or from a tape head, there is a preliminary extra stage called the preamplifier. It supplies extra amplification because the signal from such sources is ordinarily very small—in the order of millivolts instead of volts as in the case of high-level sources. The preamplifier also supplies frequency equalization to achieve flat response; bass boost and treble cut are supplied for a magnetic phono cartridge, while only bass boost is applied to the signal from a tape head.

The selector switch chooses from the various signal sources connected to the amplifier. These include tuner, tape machine, TV

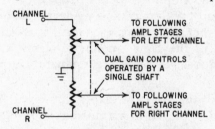

Fig. 802. *A ganged balance control featuring infinite attenuation. As the level of one channel increases, the level of the other decreases in proportion.*

and ceramic phono pickup as high-level sources (producing signals of 0.5 volt or more) and magnetic phono pickup, tape head and perhaps microphone as low-level sources. The selected signal passes through a gain control. This consists of a resistance with an arm that can be moved to any point between the incoming signal and ground, so that as the arm moves down (toward ground) the amount of signal that gets through is decreased. After the gain control, there is a stage of amplification, a loudness control (to offset the seeming disappearance of bass and treble at low levels by automatically providing bass and treble boost at reduced volume levels), tone controls, further amplification and a low-impedance circuit (usually a cathode follower) which permits the use of a long cable between the control and power amplifiers without a significant loss of high frequencies.

Shown in dashed-lines are boxes having several additional functions often, but not always, found in control amplifiers: (1) A rumble filter that sharply attenuates the low frequencies, below 60 cycles or so, to reduce low-frequency noises produced by a turntable. (2) A noise filter that sharply attenuates the high frequencies to minimize noise from scratchy records, a tape with an exces-

149

sive amount of hiss, or a tuner with a high noise level. Usually provision is made for sharp cutoff above any one of several frequencies, such as 5,000, 8,000 and 10,000 cycles. (3) A presence control that boosts the frequencies in the region of 2,000 to 5,000 cycles to inject a purportedly more lifelike quality to either music or speech.

In any given control amplifier, the sequence of functions is not necessarily the same as in Fig. 801. However, Fig. 801 is sufficiently representative for present purposes.

Balance between channels

Unique to stereo amplifiers is the balance control, permitting the listener to adjust with one knob the levels of the two channels relative to each other. Generally, each speaker should, on the average, produce about the same amount of acoustic power so that sound does not appear to come predominantly from the right or from the left.

Fig. 802 shows the basic principle employed by most stereo amplifiers for balance control, permitting the level of one channel to be increased while the other is simultaneously decreased, meanwhile maintaining the *combined* level of the two channels approximately constant. It would be more difficult to balance the two channels with respect to each other if total volume level (from the speakers) were varying at the same time that the level of one speaker was changing relative to the other. As shown in Fig. 802, two gain controls are operated by a single shaft. The connections are such that, as the arm of one control approaches ground and thereby reduces the signal level, the arm of the other control approaches the incoming signal and increases the level.

In a minority of stereo amplifiers, the balance control is omitted and individual gain controls are provided for each channel. While balance can, of course, be achieved by separate gain controls, there are two disadvantages in this procedure: (1) It does not facilitate keeping the total sound level constant while adjusting the relative level between channels. This makes the inter-channel adjustment somewhat more difficult. (2) When two controls instead of one are involved in equating channel levels, it is more difficult to return to a setting that represents balance. It may well happen that the balance control will be used to compensate for stereo discs, tapes or broadcasts that have improper channel balance. But the user will want to return to a position of true balance when playing other program material.

In some stereo amplifiers the balance control has a rather limited range of action. That is, maximum rotation of the control will produce as little as 6–10-db difference in level between channels. Other controls have a much greater range, as much as 40 db or even an infinite difference in level, which means that one channel can be completely shut off. The configuration of Fig. 802 is one of those that permits an infinite difference. Fig. 803 shows how the difference in level is limited in other cases. The extra resistance between each control and ground prevents the arm of the control from going all the way to ground and thereby achieving complete attenuation.

There are arguments in behalf of a balance control with a wide range of action as well as one with a limited range.

First, let us consider the case for a wide-range control. The ratio

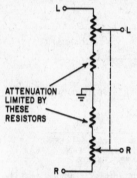

Fig. 803. *This balance control features limited attenuation. Because the range of the control is relatively narrow, it is easy to use.*

between the most and least efficient commercially available speaker systems is about 20 to 1, which is 13 db in terms of acoustic power. One may allow 6 db for differences in sensitivity of power amplifiers. For example, one power amplifier may require 1 volt to be driven to 50 watts, while another may require 2 volts, which is a difference of 6 db. One might allow a margin of another 6 db to compensate for accidental differences in level between the two channels on a disc, tape, etc. Altogether, about 25 db might be required to compensate for differences in speaker efficiency, power amplifier sensitivity and channel levels of the program source. Hence, a balance control with a range of 25 db or more is desirable and useful.

On the other hand, to the extent that one employs matched

equipment—the same speaker systems for each channel and the same power amplifiers—the need for a wide-range balance control diminishes. A range of 10 db or even less can be satisfactory under these circumstances. And there is an advantage to a limited-range balance control. Because it covers but a few db it lends itself more easily to an accurate adjustment. In other words, it has a finer vernier because each degree of rotation corresponds to only a fraction of 1 db. A balance control with a wide range, say

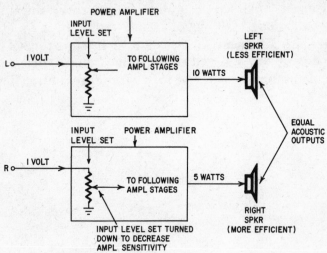

Fig. 804. *Method of adjusting power amplifier sensitivity so that equal input voltages produce equal acoustic output from matched speakers.*

40 db, is more difficult to adjust precisely because a small rotation results in a large change in level between channels.

Moreover, if speakers of different efficiencies or power amplifiers of different sensitivities are employed in the channels of a stereo system, adjustment for these differences probably should be made by other means than the balance control. Thus one might couple a more sensitive power amplifier with a less efficient speaker system, and vice versa. (Fig. 804). If the left speaker requires more power than the right for the same acoustic output, then it should be driven by the amplifier that produces more power for a given voltage input. The amount of power output for a given voltage input can be adjusted downward by the input level control found on most power amplifiers. For example, if a power amplifier will deliver 10 watts when fed 1 volt, the power output for 1 volt input can be reduced to, say, 5 watts by turning down the input level. In Fig. 804, it is assumed that the left speaker system requires 10 watts of electrical power to produce the same acoustical output as the right speaker when the latter is fed 5 watts. It is assumed that both power amplifiers can produce 10 watts for an input signal of 1 volt. Therefore, the input level control of the *right* power amplifier is turned down until an input signal of 1 volt results in only 5 watts out of this unit. By cutting down the sensitivity of the right amplifier, the final result is that equal sound levels are obtained from the speakers.

If the power amplifier–speaker combination of the left channel is balanced with that of the right channel, then the function of the balance control can be limited largely to compensating for inequalities between channels in the signal source. Accordingly, a

Fig. 805. *To balance the stereo system from a normal listening position some control amplifiers include a balance control at the end of a long cable.*

balance control with a range of 10 db or less should be adequate. Moreover, if there is balance in the rest of the system (apart from the signal source), the control can be operated to either side of

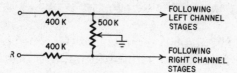

Fig. 806. *Using a single control to provide channel balance. This circuit feature infinite attenuation.*

mid-setting. If it is necessary to operate the balance control close to either extreme of its rotation to compensate for power amplifier or speaker differences, then there may not be sufficient reserve for balancing other inequalities. Finally, if balance is characteristically achieved at mid-setting, it is usually easier to return to this point than to any other setting of the control.

One problem in achieving balance is that the amplifier is usually

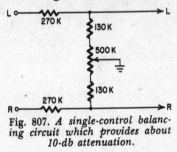

Fig. 807. *A single-control balancing circuit which provides about 10-db attenuation.*

a number of feet away from one's customary listening position. Hence what appears to be proper balance when the listener is standing next to the control amplifier may no longer appear so when he takes his favorite seat. To solve this problem, some con-

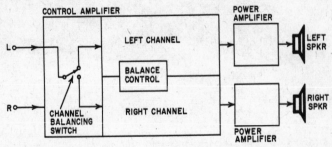

Fig. 808. *Some stereo control amplifiers include a channel balancing switch which enables the listener to switch from one channel to the other.*

trol amplifiers place the balance control at the end of an extension cable long enough to reach any point in an average-size room (Fig. 805).

While Figs. 802 and 803 indicate that two controls—although on one shaft—are required to adjust balance, it is possible to accomplish the same end by just one control, as shown in Fig. 806. As the arm of the control is moved up, the upper channel is shorted to ground; as it travels down, the lower channel is shorted. This arrangement, using the values shown, will maintain the combined sound level from the two speakers reasonably constant as the control is rotated in either direction. Fig. 807 shows a similar configuration, except that neither channel is completely attenuated;

instead, the maximum difference existing between channels is approximately 10 db.

Many stereo control amplifiers permit one to balance channels

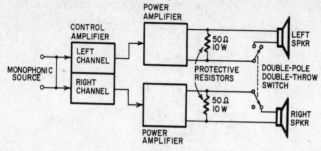

Fig. 809. *When the control amplifier does not include a channel-balancing switch, a simple circuit can be made from a dpdt switch and two resistors.*

by alternately feeding an incoming signal to one channel and then the other, as illustrated in Fig. 808. Thus, one may feed the channel L signal alternately to the left and right channels and adjust the balance control until each speaker produces apparently the same amount of sound. However, in many amplifiers there is no

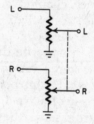

Fig. 810. *The master gain control is used to adjust overall listening level after the system has been balanced.*

such provision. The listener can then employ a simple means for balancing, as illustrated in Fig. 809. A double-pole double-throw switch alternately connects speaker L while disconnecting speaker R and connects speaker R while disconnecting speaker L. Protective resistors—a 10-watt 50-ohm unit is generally suitable—should be used to avoid the possibility of damaging the output transformer of the power amplifier when the speaker load is removed by the switch.

In Fig. 809 the signal used for balancing is from a monophonic source and is fed to both channels. However, the signal could just as well be either the left- or right-channel signal from a stereo source. Virtually all control amplifiers permit feeding a monophonic signal into both channels.

155

Master gain control

Once the listener has adjusted his system for proper balance between the two stereo channels, he must be able to change over-all volume level without upsetting this interchannel balance.

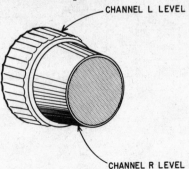

CHANNEL L LEVEL

CHANNEL R LEVEL

Fig. 811. *Instead of tying the gain controls for each channel together, many stereo amplifiers use concentric units.*

Therefore stereo amplifiers contain a master gain control such as that shown in Fig. 810. Essentially it consists of two gain controls, one for each channel, mounted on a single shaft. It is similar to the balance control of Fig. 802 except that, in the master gain control the levels of both channels vary in the same direction instead of in opposite directions.

In a few stereo amplifiers, instead of a master gain control there are individual controls for each channel, particularly where a balance control as such is not provided. That is, the individual gain controls serve the dual purpose of balancing the channels and governing the total sound level. However, the tendency in this case is to mount the controls concentrically (Fig. 811), with the inner knob controlling one channel and the outer knob the other. It is then possible to achieve the effect of a master gain control by rotating both knobs together. Carrying this one step further, some amplifiers use concentric gain controls that lock together when the inner knob is pushed in slightly; when it is pulled out, the controls operate independently. Fig. 812 is a drawing of a "push-pull" concentric pair of axially-aligned controls illustrating the locking feature.

Once balance between channels has been achieved, it should not be changed when increasing or decreasing total gain. Any change in balance which occurs when rotating a master gain control is referred to as tracking error. Obviously, a minimum of tracking error is desirable for stereo; preferably it should be no more than 1 db. A tracking error of this amount means, for example, that as one rotates the master gain control, assuming perfect balance

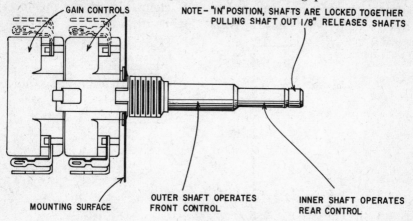

GAIN CONTROLS

NOTE— "IN" POSITION, SHAFTS ARE LOCKED TOGETHER
PULLING SHAFT OUT 1/8" RELEASES SHAFTS

MOUNTING SURFACE

OUTER SHAFT OPERATES
FRONT CONTROL

INNER SHAFT OPERATES
REAR CONTROL

Fig. 812. *To facilitate setting overall level, this type of concentric control uses a special mechanism to permit the shafts to be locked together.*

to start with, the difference between levels of the two channels will not exceed 1 db at any setting of the control.

When using ordinary gain controls mounted on a single shaft,

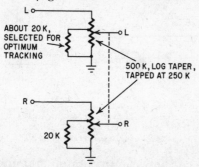

L

ABOUT 20 K,
SELECTED FOR
OPTIMUM
TRACKING

L

500 K, LOG TAPER,
TAPPED AT 250 K

R

R

20 K

Fig. 813. *To insure accurate tracking, tapped gain controls are often used.*

it is possible to have a tracking error of as much as 5 db or more. If the channel levels are exactly matched when the master gain control is at maximum position, at lower settings there may be a difference between levels of 5 db or more. However, manufacturers of stereo amplifiers minimize tracking error in several ways.

One method is to use gain controls manufactured to close tolerances. Another is to use run-of-the-mill controls but selected to form matched pairs having similar characteristics (tapers). A third way is to use taps, as shown in Fig. 813, to bring the two controls into correspondence at several intermediate points. The resistors connected from the taps to ground are chosen so that each control provides the same amount of attenuation at one or more intermediate points of arm travel. Hence the amount of tracking

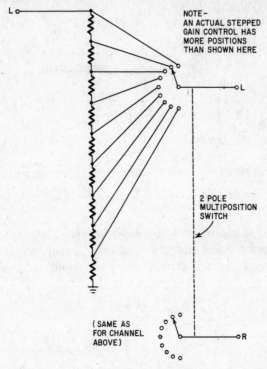

NOTE–
AN ACTUAL STEPPED
GAIN CONTROL HAS
MORE POSITIONS
THAN SHOWN HERE

2 POLE
MULTIPOSITION
SWITCH

(SAME AS
FOR CHANNEL
ABOVE)

Fig. 814. *Stepped master gain controls produce a tracking error of less than 1% when precision resistors are used.*

error that can occur between maximum and minimum settings of the master gain control is limited.

A fourth method of minimizing tracking error is to use what are known as stepped controls (Fig. 814). The stepped control consists of a series string of resistors, with the top of the string and each junction between successive resistors connected to terminals on a multiposition switch. The arm of the switch behaves like the arm on the variable control, except that it moves in discrete steps. The values of the resistors are chosen so that as the switch is turned from one position to the next, the change in volume is a fixed amount, usually about 2 or 3 db. Using precision resistors or matched resistors of the ordinary variety, tracking error can easily be kept well under 1%.

The stepped control has several disadvantages. It is considerably

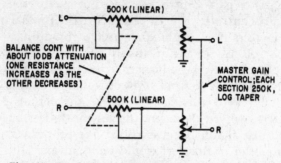

Fig. 815. *To place the master gain and balance controls in an early stage, some amplifiers use combined controls.*

more expensive than the variable control. It does not provide as full a range of volume adjustment. Whereas the variable control can provide attenuation over an infinite range, the stepped control, because of the necessarily limited number of switch positions,

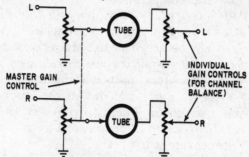

Fig. 816. *Some amplifiers separate the master gain and the balance controls by a single stage.*

is limited to an attenuation range of about 45 or 50 db. However, in most circumstances such a range should be sufficient.

Location of gain control

Gain controls are best located at an early stage in the control amplifier, as shown in Fig. 801. Thus, the signal is reduced before it has a chance to drive any stage hard enough to cause significant distortion. It is desirable to have not only the master gain control but also the balance control at an early stage, rather than have one or the other at a later stage. Therefore in a number of control amplifiers the master gain and balance controls are brought together in the manner of Fig. 815.

Fig. 816 represents a situation that occurs in some stereo amplifiers. The master gain control is located at an early stage but individual gain controls for each channel, used for balancing purposes, are located after a subsequent stage of amplification. If the balance controls are set at a relatively low position, then the master gain control must be advanced to a correspondingly higher position to produce a desired level of sound. If the listener likes his music fairly loud, this may mean that the master gain control is advanced to where the signal drives the following stage hard enough to cause significant distortion. The proper way to operate a stereo amplifier of this sort would be to advance the individual gain controls as far as possible consistent with balance between channels, and then set the master gain control for the desired overall volume level; with the individual controls well advanced, the master gain control will be at a correspondingly reduced position, limiting the signal to the following stage.

This procedure may raise a problem if the master gain control incorporates loudness compensation. If the individual gain controls are well advanced, then the master gain control may have to be operated at so low a position as to produce excessive loudness compensation. It may be necessary to reduce the setting of the individual gain controls, permitting the master gain control to be set higher, which means less loudness compensation. Or, perhaps as a desirable alternative, one may disable the loudness-compensation feature—most stereo amplifiers provide a switch for doing so —and rely upon the bass and treble controls to provide the desired frequency reinforcement at low levels.

Tone controls

It is open to question whether or not the bass and treble controls of the two channels should be operated ganged, as in the case of the master gain control.

The ganged tone control simplifies operation and appearance. On the other hand, the individual tone control for each channel permits greater flexibility, making it easier to meet the foreseeable and unforeseeable problems that arise in stereo reproduction. If the stereophile uses different speaker systems for the two channels, he may well find it necessary to provide different amounts of bass and treble correction in each channel to obtain the best possible balance. Even when using matched speaker systems, their location and orientation with respect to the listener may call for different kinds and quantities of tonal correction. Furthermore, differences in the signal source may call for different bass and treble adjustment on each channel. Thus, when receiving a stereo program via FM–AM, one will very likely wish to apply treble boost in greater quantity only to the AM signal to correct for the usual treble deficiency on this channel. Or the tonal characteristics may differ from channel to channel on a stereo tape or disc.

Altogether, it seems that, at the present stage of stereo development, a stronger case can be made for separate tone controls for each channel than for ganged ones. However, with further advances, including the transition from FM–AM stereo broadcasts to FM multiplex, with greater use of matched speaker systems and greater uniformity of frequency response on each channel of stereo discs and stereo tapes, it is to be expected that the present advantages of a separate tone control will become less pronounced.

Loudness control

In monophonic control amplifiers, the classical means of loudness compensation (Fig. 801) has been a separate control called the loudness control. This introduces substantial quantities of bass boost and moderate quantities (sometimes none at all) of treble boost as volume is reduced. The purpose of the gain control is to adjust the volume so that at the maximum position of the loudness control the sound level corresponds approximately to that of the original performance. Thereafter, one uses the loudness control to govern volume, so that as volume is reduced from the original performance level, bass and treble boost are introduced to compensate for the seeming loss of bass and treble.

Because of the complexity of a stereo amplifier, most manufacturers have eliminated separate gain and loudness controls. The general practice is to incorporate a switch that converts the master gain control into a loudness control. In the off position of this switch, the master gain control increases or decreases the level equally for all frequencies. In the on position of the switch, various frequencies are boosted or attenuated by different amounts, so that at a low setting of the control there is, in effect, bass and treble boost; the lower the setting, the greater the boost.

Unfortunately, the use of a loudness control without a separate gain control does not enable one to equate the maximum setting of the loudness control with original performance levels. This raises a problem: the loudness control may produce too much or too little loudness compensation. Sometimes the situation can be handled by using the volume control on a radio tuner or tape playback machine to perform the same function as a separate gain control on the amplifier. But this is not always possible or practical, especially in the case of a phono pickup, which has no gain control. Therefore, the user of a stereo amplifier may find he fares

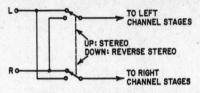

Fig. 817. *A channel-reversing switch is sometimes included in stereo amplifiers.*

best by putting the loudness switch in the off position and by using the bass and treble controls for loudness compensation.

Channel switching

While the basic function of a stereo control amplifier is to accept the channel L and R signals from a source, such as disc or tape,

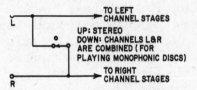

Fig. 818. *Switch for combining the outputs of stereo amplifiers for monophonic listening.*

and feed them to the respective L and R power amplifiers and speaker systems, it nevertheless should be able to perform a number of switching functions to permit balancing channels, listening to monophonic sources, correcting for errors in phasing or channel identification in the source, etc. There are various switching arrangements likely to be useful to the stereophile. While most stereo amplifiers provide the majority of these arrangements, very few provide all of them.

Reverse stereo

This permits the L signal to be fed to the right channel and the R signal to the left one, as in Fig. 817. If the channels are reversed on a disc or tape, the listener will have to undo the mistake. While it is to be expected that such reversals will ultimately be eliminated, the need for channel reversal will continue for other reasons. For one thing, amateur recordists, playing their own tapes or those of friends, will probably not reduce their mistakes to the same extent as professionals. More important, no standardization exists yet as to whether the FM or AM portion of an FM–AM stereocast is to be reproduced by the left speaker. The same holds for the two channels on a multiplex stereo broadcast. While

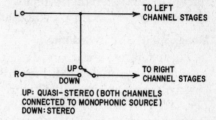

Fig. 819. *A quasi-stereo switch for obtaining a stereo effect from monophonic source material.*

UP: QUASI-STEREO (BOTH CHANNELS CONNECTED TO MONOPHONIC SOURCE)
DOWN: STEREO

standardization is bound to occur eventually, it is far enough in the future to justify a channel-reversing function at present. Finally, the experimentally inclined stereophile may well be curious as to the effects of reversing channels when there is no need to do

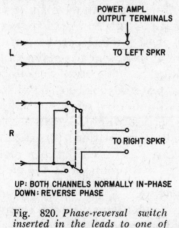

UP: BOTH CHANNELS NORMALLY IN-PHASE
DOWN: REVERSE PHASE

Fig. 820. *Phase-reversal switch inserted in the leads to one of the stereo speakers.*

so. Conceivably, for certain types of music or in special circumstances, reversal may enhance the appeal of the music. Thus, in a case that came to the attention of the author, several persons found that reproduction of a specific selection of organ music was improved by reversing channels, even though channel reversal had not accidentally taken place at the source.

Balance switching

This permits the L signal to be fed either to the left or right channel as illustrated in Fig. 808. Alternately switching the signal from one channel to the other facilitates balancing the sound levels of the two speaker systems. Where the control amplifier incorporates reverse stereo switching, separate balance switching is not strictly necessary, because reverse stereo accomplishes the same thing, provided one disconnects the R signal source from the amplifier. However, having to remove the R signal may at times prove inconvenient, as when playing a stereo disc.

Monophonic disc switching

This combines the L and R signals and feeds the combined signal to both channels, as in Fig. 818. Or else the outputs of the two channels are combined just before the output of the control amplifier. This is desirable when playing a monophonic disc with a stereo cartridge. It is true that each channel of the stereo cartridge delivers the same audio signal, so that reproducing the signal from either channel will provide the entire sound. However, two benefits are gained from combining the signals. (1) Vertical rumble, generally more serious than horizontal rumble, is cancelled to a substantial degree. The two channels of a stereo cartridge ordinarily have their outputs in phase with respect to lateral stylus motion and out of phase with respect to vertical motion. When playing a monophonic disc, which contains only lateral program information, the outputs of the two sections are in phase with respect to program material and out of phase with respect to rumble due to vertical motion. Hence the audio signals are added in phase, while the vertical rumble signals are added out of phase to produce appreciable cancellation. (2) Greater signal output is obtained from the cartridge, resulting in a higher signal-to-noise ratio provided the noise is produced by the amplifier.

Quasi-stereo switching

This feeds the L (or R) signal to each channel, as in Fig. 819, permitting one to hear a monophonic source on both speaker systems, thus supplying a quasi-stereo effect. While a system that provides monophonic disc switching in a sense also permits quasi-stereo switching, the reverse is not true. In some stereo amplifiers one can feed the L signal to both channels, but not the R signal at the same time.

Phase reversal

This permits the phase of one channel to be reversed with respect to the other. Where the stereo amplifier contains a power amplifier, this is most easily accomplished by reversing the leads to one set of speaker terminals, as in Fig. 820. Where the unit is only a control amplifier, it must be accomplished electronically (Fig. 821). The signal at the grid of a voltage amplifying tube is opposite in phase to that at the plate. Hence, the signal of one of the channels is passed through an extra tube stage, causing the signal to change phase by 180°. Any amplification that takes place can be offset by a voltage attenuator before the tube. While disc

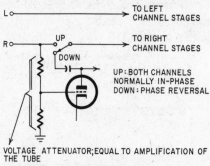

Fig. 821. *An electronic phase-reversing switch which can be included in a control amplifier.*

and tape program sources are careful to maintain proper phasing, the unpredictable consequences of microphone and speaker placement make it possible that changing the phase of one channel relative to the other will result in better sound. Moreover, it is possible that phasing mistakes in recording stereo sound will be made by the amateur and even the professional. Accordingly, a phase-reversal switch can be of service. Incorrect phasing of the sounds from the two speaker systems will result in improper spatial orientation, particularly of sounds that are supposed to come from an area about midway between the speakers.

All of the switching functions are usually performed by one switch, except for phase reversal. In some control amplifiers, however, several switches may be employed.

Blend control

One of the major problems that tend to occur in stereo is the apparent absence of sound in the space between two speakers. The more widely separated the microphones in the recording process or the more widely separated the speakers in the home, the more one is likely to be conscious of "hole-in-the-center" effect.

One way to reduce this effect is to feed some of the L signal to the right channel and some of the R signal to the left channel, thereby decreasing the difference in the nature of the sound coming from the left and the right. The more similar the sounds from each speaker system, the less pronounced will tend to be the hole in the center.

The blend control provides this mixing function, permitting the listener to combine the left and right signals to any extent. Illustrated in Fig. 822, this control consists simply of a variable resistance linking the two channels. The resistance is sufficiently great so that, when the arm is at the top position, there is insignificant blending of the two signals. But, as the arm is moved down,

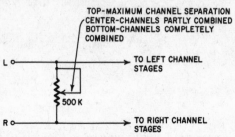

Fig. 822. *A blend control which is used to help eliminate the hole-in-the-center effect.*

the resistance between the upper and lower channels decreases, resulting in a partial blending of the two signals. At minimum position of the arm, the two channels are completely combined, achieving the same result then as the monophonic disc switching function.

Phantom channel output

A more substantial step toward eliminating the hole in the center is to combine the left and right signals to feed a third, central speaker. The left and right signals so combined are referred to as a phantom channel; at the same time the original channels are preserved for feeding the left and right speaker systems.

Fig. 823 shows the basic method employed in some control amplifiers to provide a phantom (center) channel output. Two resistors in series are connected between the left- and right-channel outputs, and the junction of these two resistors feeds the phantom-channel output. In other words, they link the center channel to the left and right channels, and at the same time are sufficiently high in value to isolate the left and right channels from each other.

The technique of Fig. 823 utilizes a fixed ratio between the L and R signals. If the balance control is set so that one channel, say L, produces more signal than the other (perhaps to compensate for lower efficiency on the part of the left speaker system), then the phantom channel would have more L content than R content. Therefore, it becomes all the more important to adjust the stereo

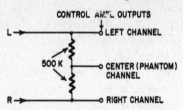

CONTROL AMPL OUTPUTS

Fig. 823. *Some control amplifiers include this type of circuitry to provide a phantom-channel output.*

system (Fig. 804) so that equal signals in the L and R channels result in equal sound from the L and R speakers. Consequently, adjustment of the balance control for equal sound from the speakers will mean signals of equal level in the L and R channels, resulting in a phantom-channel signal containing equal parts of L and R.

There are reasons why one may want to have control over the proportions in which L and R are combined for the center channel. For example, a dominantly left signal in the phantom channel may be desired because the center speaker cannot be located exactly midway between the other two, but must be situated closer to the left speaker because of problems of decor.

Fig. 824 shows a circuit that permits such control. Instead of having two fixed resistors a variable resistance is used, with the arm going to the center channel. As the arm moves above center, the phantom-channel signal consists primarily of L. In mid-position of the arm, there are equal parts of L and R. As the arm moves below center, the phantom channel consists primarily of R.

Inputs

A stereo amplifier should have at least three pairs of high-level inputs (for sources producing 0.5 volt or more): one pair for tuners, a second for a piezoelectric stereo cartridge (ceramic or crystal), and a third for a stereo tape machine. A fourth pair may be desirable as an auxiliary for other sources, such as television sound.

Pay particular attention to the input jacks that may be specifically designated for a piezoelectric cartridge. Stereo has increased the popularity of this type, inherently simpler in construction and less costly to manufacture than magnetic stereo cartridges, and at the same time affording good performance. However, the piezo-electric cartridge has special loading problems, not always recognized by manufacturers of control amplifiers (mono or stereo). Typically, it requires a load resistance of about 2 megohms—the range is from 1 to 3 megohms, depending upon the make—to achieve relatively flat response in the bass region. Loads much below 1 or 2 megohms result in loss of bass. However, high-level input jacks often present a load of only 510,000 ohms to the source. Therefore, for use with a piezoelectric stereo pickup, the stereo amplifier must provide a suitable load resistance for the particular cartridge. If it doesn't, the correct value of load resistance can easily and quickly be inserted.

Some control amplifiers have a special circuit designed to convert a piezoelectric pickup into the equivalent of a magnetic cartridge in the sense that the signal will exhibit the same frequency response characteristic (drooping bass and rising treble) as a magnetic cartridge and will therefore employ the same playback equalization. If this is true of the input marked "piezoelec-

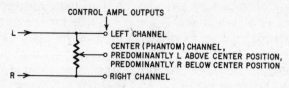

Fig. 824. *A phantom-channel output circuit with provision for variable mixing.*

tric pickup," it is necessary to ascertain that the conversion circuit is suitable for the particular pickup to be used. This information can be obtained from the manufacturer of the pickup. If a modification is necessary, again it can easily be made by a technician in accordance with the instructions of the cartridge manufacturer.

Included in the low-level inputs should be provision not only for magnetic stereo cartridges, but also for signals directly from a stereo tape playback head. Some control amplifiers provide a third pair of low-level inputs to accommodate microphones.

The output of a magnetic stereo cartridge tends to be appreciably lower than that of its mono counterpart because of design problems inherent in a stereo pickup and because of the lower levels recorded on stereo discs. Therefore, the stereo amplifier should have extra sensitivity so that the signal delivered by the stereo magnetic cartridge will be amplified to a level sufficient to

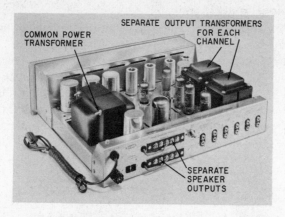

COMMON POWER TRANSFORMER

SEPARATE OUTPUT TRANSFORMERS FOR EACH CHANNEL

SEPARATE SPEAKER OUTPUTS

Fig. 825. *A typical stereo power amplifier consists of two separate units on a single chassis. Note the relatively uncluttered nature of the circuitry in the lower illustration.* (Courtesy H. H. Scott, Inc.)

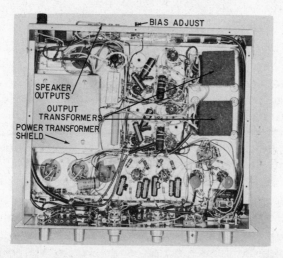

BIAS ADJUST

SPEAKER OUTPUTS

OUTPUT TRANSFORMERS

POWER TRANSFORMER SHIELD

drive a power amplifier or the speaker system. That is, the stereo amplifier should be able to deliver at least 1 volt to a power amplifier or the rated power output (10 watts or more) to a speaker when the signal from the cartridge is 5 millivolts at 1,000 cycles.

The sensitivity—signal output for a given signal input—should be somewhat greater for the tape-head input, because tape playback heads, particularly of the four-track variety, deliver appreciably less signal than magnetic phono cartridges. Accordingly, no more than 2 millivolts input at 1,000 cycles should be required for adequate output by the stereo amplifier.

Stereo power amplifiers

Compared with the stereo control amplifier, the power amplifier has tended to be a relatively unsophisticated piece of apparatus, generally consisting of two power amplifiers on a single chassis (Fig. 825). The basic advantage of such a unit over two individual power amplifiers is a saving in cost and space inasmuch as a single power supply can accommodate both amplifiers. Moreover, there may be some merit in the fact that the amplifiers are

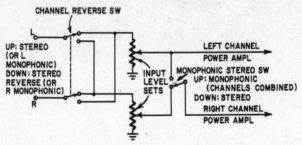

Fig. 826. *Basic channel-switching circuits.*

matched, having the same power output, frequency response and other characteristics. On the other hand, if the stereo system employs two speaker systems of substantially different efficiency, the matched power output may be somewhat of a disadvantage because an inefficient speaker requires more electrical power. Thus, one speaker may require 30 watts (on peaks) whereas another may need only 5 watts for the same acoustic output. It is unlikely, if the power amplifiers are matched, that one can deliver 30 watts at distortion as low as when the other is delivering 5 watts.

Stereo power amplifiers generally provide basic channel-switching facilities. Fig. 826 shows what they are. A CHANNEL REVERSE switch serves the same function as the reverse stereo switch in Fig. 817. A MONOPHONIC–STEREO switch serves same function as the quasi-stereo switch in Fig. 819, permitting the left (or right) signal to be fed to both channels.

Sometimes the stereo power amplifier has a switch that parallels both output stages, as in Fig. 827. Thus the total power that can be fed to a monophonic speaker system is doubled.

Where no paralleling switch is provided, the listener may easily shunt the output stages in the manner of Fig. 828. It is assumed here that the monophonic speaker has an impedance of

16 ohms. When the output transformers are paralleled, their combined impedance is half that of either one alone. Therefore,

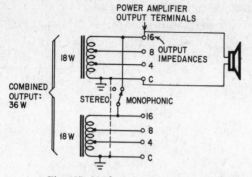

Fig. 827. *Method of connecting a monophonic speaker system to both outputs of a stereo power amplifier.*

to match the 16-ohm speaker impedance, it is necessary to parallel the 32-ohm impedance taps. Ordinarily, high-fidelity power amplifiers do not provide output impedances higher than 16 ohms. But

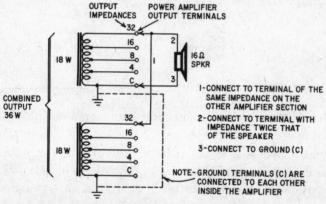

Fig. 828. *When no paralleling switch is provided in the stereo power amplifier, shunt the output stages as shown.*

some stereo amplifiers do have transformers providing 32-ohm taps. (If it were necessary to match an 8-ohm speaker, no problem would exist: the 16-ohm output taps would then be paralleled.) Fig. 828 shows that three connections are required. The 32-ohm taps on the two output transformers are connected to each other. One speaker lead is connected to the 32-ohm tap on either output transformer. The other speaker lead is connected to ground.

A new, sophisticated approach to the stereo power amplifier is represented in Fig. 829. Like a conventional monophonic power amplifier, it employs just two output tubes and one output transformer, rather than four output tubes and two transformers. The difference-frequency principle is applied in a manner similar to

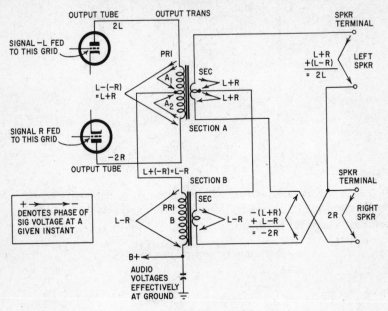

Fig. 829. *CBS simplex stereo power amplifier using only two output tubes.*

that already described in connection with stereo on the air, stereo on discs and stereo microphones.

Assume that a —L signal is fed to the grid of the upper tube and an R signal to the lower tube. The phase of a signal at the plate is opposite to that at the grid. Therefore, an L signal appears at the plate of the upper tube and a —R signal at the plate of the lower tube. For ease of explanation, let us assume that the signal voltage at the upper plate is 2L and that at the lower plate is —2R.

Fig. 829 shows that the output transformer is in two sections, A and B; A in turn is divided into A_1 and A_2. Each section has a primary, which is connected to the tubes, and a secondary, which feeds the stereo speakers. Let us first consider the signals across the primary windings. The 2L signal (between plate and ground) divides itself between primary windings A_1 and B (B is effectively at ground for audio voltages), hence contributing voltage L to each of these windings; similarly, the −2R signal contributes voltage −R to primary windings A_2 and B. The total voltage across primary winding A (namely windings A_1 and A_2 in series) is the difference between the voltage at the top and bottom of A, namely L − (−R), which is L + R. The total voltage across primary winding B is the sum of the signals there, namely L + (−R), which is L − R.

By transformer action, signal L − R is present across secondary winding B, and L + R across each of the secondary windings of A_1 and A_2. The voltage of secondary B is combined with the voltage of the secondary of A_2 *out of phase*, producing (L − R) + (−L −R), which is −2R. Then −2R is converted to 2R by reversing the leads to the speaker terminals. The voltage of secondary B is combined with the voltage of the secondary of A_1 *in phase*, producing (L − R) + (L + R), which is 2L. This is fed to the other set of speaker terminals.

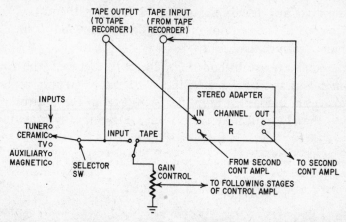

Fig. 830. *The tape-monitor switch on a monophonic control amplifier can be used for the connection of a stereo adapter.*

To the extent that the L and R signals are similar, which is ordinarily considerable in view of the fact that the two signals are generated by the same source of sound, the value L + R will be substantially greater than the value L − R. The tubes in Fig. 829 operate in conventional push-pull fashion for L + R signals. This method of operation can handle greater amounts of power at low distortion than if the tubes were operating in parallel fashion. But since the amount of power contained in the L −

R signal will ordinarily be much less than in the L + R signal, this tends to compensate for the fact that the tubes are operating in parallel rather than push-pull for L − R signals. Low frequencies, where the problem of distortion tends to be most acute, are primarily in phase (L + R), so that they are handled by the output tubes in push-pull fashion, which results in least distortion.

The circuit of Fig. 829 makes possible an appreciable reduction in the cost and size of a stereo power amplifier. Conceivably, there may be similar developments in control amplifiers that will reduce the complicated structure of the present units.

Stereo adapters

The foregoing sections have discussed three types of stereo amplifiers: control amplifiers; integrated amplifiers—control amplifiers combined with power amplifiers; power amplifiers. A fourth category consists of units designed to adapt two conventional control or integrated amplifiers to stereo use. Several such adapters on the market provide a master gain control, channel-switching facilities and, on occasion, a blend control. A balance control is often not included because the mono amplifiers each have a gain control.

Some adapters are intended for insertion between the control amplifier and the power amplifier. Others, to permit reduction of signal level before the amplification stages of the control amplifier and thereby minimize distortion, are specifically intended for

Fig. 831. *A special stereo adapter and two control amplifiers. This type of adapter is actually inserted between tape output and input circuits. It also performs as a standard stereo adapter for use with other signal sources.* (Courtesy of H. H. Scott, Inc.)

use with any control or integrated amplifier that contains a TAPE MONITOR switch (Fig. 830). In such a control amplifier, the output from a tape machine is not fed to the amplifier in the same manner as other signal sources, such as a tuner. Instead, the tape-monitor switch feeds the tape-machine signal to the amplifier.

Fig. 832. *A rear view of the adapter shown in Fig. 831. The unit contains facilities for connection to monophonic amplifiers and for feeding and accepting signals from a tape machine.* (Courtesy H. H. Scott, Inc.)

In the tape position of the switch, the amplifier is connected to the output of the tape machine. In the other position, the amplifier is connected to the selector switch that chooses among the tuner, phono, TV, etc. inputs. At the same time, the selector switch is *always* connected to a tape output jack for feeding a signal *into* a tape recorder.

This arrangement makes it possible to insert the stereo adapter in series between the tape output and input jacks. All signals coming into the control amplifier are routed into the stereo adapter via the tape output jack; and signals coming out of the adapter are routed through the tape input jack to the gain control, tone control, filter, etc. stages of the amplifier. To do so requires setting the tape-monitor switch to the TAPE position. Fig. 831 is a photo of a stereo adapter that has been combined with two control amplifiers suitable for the purpose.

Because the stereo adapter pre-empts the tape output and input facilities of the control amplifier, the adapter must provide such facilities. Fig. 832 is a rear view of an adapter, showing the various jacks for connecting the adapter to the mono amplifiers and for feeding signals to and accepting signals from a tape recorder.

The stereo adapter can be employed with mono control amplifiers that do not have a tape monitor switch, by making a suitable modification in the control amplifiers, a fairly simple task for an audio technician. The modification consists of interrupting the signal path between the selector switch and the next stage, and routing the signal through the adapter as shown in Fig. 830.

speakers for stereo

W HAT has been said many times about monophonic reproduction is at least as true for stereo: In the last analysis, the sound must come from a speaker system, and too much importance cannot be attached to this, the final link in the audio reproduction chain. In the early excitement over stereo, not too much attention was given to matters such as speaker quality, matching, placement, phasing, etc. So long as two speakers placed several feet apart were employed, that was considered stereo. Enough time has now passed to permit a fuller appreciation of the factors that must be given close attention if a stereo speaker system is to equal and then surpass monophonic systems in the ultimate test—pleasing the listener.

Speaker placement

Optimum location of speakers for stereo depends upon four basic factors: (1) the manner in which the microphones were placed in recording; (2) the dimensions and acoustic properties of the listening room; (3) the listener's position in the room; (4) the radiation pattern of the speakers used.

It is common practice to space the microphones so they are on the lines of an angle formed by a desirable listening point with the extremes of the music source (see Fig. 705). In playback, the objective is to have the speakers in the home form the same angle with respect to the listener. This angle is usually between 30° and 45°. Consequently, placement of the speakers so that their axes form an angle of 30° to 45° with the listener is likely to produce satisfactory results.

This does not mean that the only suitable listening position is the convergence of the lines forming an angle of 30° to 45° from the speakers. If the listener moves about the room, the

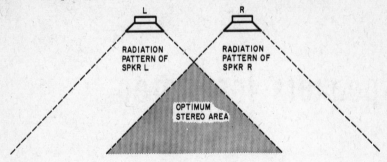

Fig. 901. *To receive the benefits of the stereo effect, the listener must position himself in an area where the radiation patterns of the speakers overlap.*

stereo effect will not be destroyed but altered, much as the character of the sound that one hears in a concert hall, night club, etc. changes according to one's location. The important

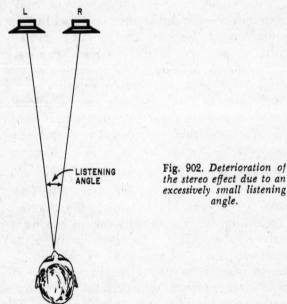

Fig. 902. *Deterioration of the stereo effect due to an excessively small listening angle.*

thing is that the listener be within the radiation pattern of both speakers (Fig. 901). Most authorities agree that, once the listener is far enough from the speakers to be within the radiation pattern of both, he will experience the stereo sensation. On the other hand, if he is so far back that the angle he forms with the speakers is only a few degrees (Fig. 902), then the stereo effect deteriorates. Stated differently, as the distance from listener to

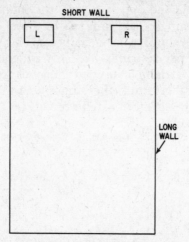

Fig. 903. *Recommended position
for stereo speakers.*

speakers is increased, their sounds tend to fuse, providing one instead of the two sources required.

Best spacing of the speakers depends upon the dimensions of

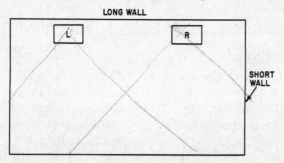

Fig. 904. *Typical placement of a stereo speaker system
against the long wall of a room.*

the room and whether the speakers are placed against the short or long wall, assuming the room is rectangular rather than square. For ease of discussion, we shall think in terms of a rectangular room or else the rectangular portion of a room that is otherwise shaped.

It is often recommended that the speakers be placed against the short wall (Fig. 903) so that they face the long dimension of the room. This may not always be possible because of problems of decor, positions of doors or windows, etc. When speakers are a short distance from the opposite wall, the sound waves reflecting from the wall tend to combine with those coming from the speakers either to reinforce or partially cancel the latter, producing an uneven frequency response. Which frequencies are reinforced and which are partially cancelled depends upon the distance between the speakers and the opposite wall. If the wall is heavily draped, the deleterious effects will be reduced.

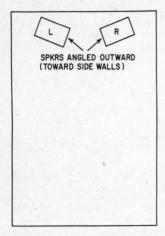

SPKRS ANGLED OUTWARD
(TOWARD SIDE WALLS)

Fig. 905 (left). *Method of compensating for close speaker placement.*

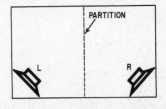

Fig. 906 (above). *Placement of stereo speakers within a single cabinet.*

When the stereo speakers are against the short wall, best results tend to be obtained by a relatively wide spacing (Fig. 903). Thus even for a listener well toward the rear of the room, the angle between him and the speakers will be fairly wide. Excessively wide spacing reduces the area that falls within the radiation pattern of both speakers, limiting the portion of the room suitable for stereo listening. Of course, a factor here is the radiation pattern of the particular speakers used.

When the stereo speakers are spaced against the long wall, do not place them too far apart. Typical good spacing is shown in Fig. 904. If the speakers are too far apart, not only is the area common to the radiation patterns of both speakers seriously restricted, but a substantial hole-in-the-center effect tends to apear.

For one reason or another, it may be necessary to place the stereo speakers so close together as to form a relatively narrow angle with the listener. However, one can compensate by angling the speakers outward, as in Fig. 905. Such placement has been found capable of quite satisfactory stereo results and is sometimes the basis for inclusion of two speaker systems within a single

Fig. 907. *A stereo speaker system in which the stereo effect is produced by speakers which face away from each other by 180°.* (Courtesy R. T. Bozak Sales Co.)

cabinet (Fig. 906). Fig. 907 shows a single-cabinet stereo speaker system in which the speakers face 180° away from each other. This is extreme angling. However, the sound reflects from a partially open door on each side, so that it actually angles off in a manner similar to that in Fig. 906. Fig. 908 shows another method of incorporating two stereo speaker systems in a single cabinet. Much of the audio range, particularly that which is associated with the stereo effect, is produced by the horn-loaded speakers that partly face each other; their sound is deflected by the large wooden curved surface. Other methods exist of incorporating stereo speakers in one enclosure, and doubtless the future will bring still more.

Corner placement

There has been a good deal of discussion as to the merits of corner placement of stereo speakers. For monophonic repro-

Fig. 908. *A stereo speaker system in which the stereo effect is produced by the horn-loaded units partially facing each other.* (Courtesy James B. Lansing Sound, Inc.)

duction, corner placement is usually satisfactory and often the best position for a number of reasons. Only a 90° radiation pattern is needed to cover the entire room; the corner reinforces the reproduction of bass frequencies by acting as a horn and the speaker does not directly face a wall, so that the problem of reinforcing and cancelling sound waves is mitigated. For stereo, however, there are arguments con as well as pro.

One point of view is that corner speakers tend to localize the stereo effect into a relatively small area (Fig. 909). On the other hand, it is argued, corner placement causes virtually the entire room to be within the radiation pattern of both speakers (Fig.

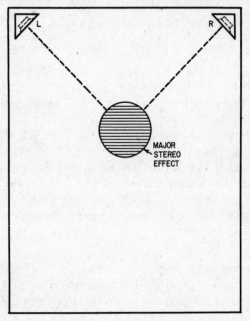

Fig. 909. *A localization of the stereo effect is attributed to the use of corner speakers.*

910). Which of these views is correct depends upon the room in which the corner speakers are used, upon the arrangement of the components in each speaker system and upon the radiation patterns of these components.

If the room has fairly hard reflecting surfaces, such as undraped walls and bare floors, the middle and high frequencies will tend to be dispersed in a manner that causes the stereo effect to be more widespread. The basic reason why corner speakers are considered to produce the localized pattern of Fig. 909 is that at high frequencies the radiation pattern of a speaker tends to form a "beam" of sound. To get away from this beaming effect, it is considered desirable to have the mid-range speakers and tweeters face straight down the room (Fig. 911) instead of

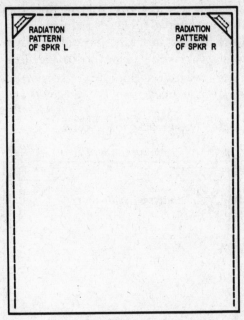

Fig. 910. *The radiation pattern attributed to corner speakers.*

angling inward in the manner of the woofer. The low frequencies produced by the woofer are essentially nondirectional and therefore little, if at all, associated with the stereo effect, at least so far as directionality is concerned. Most speaker systems for corner use are designed to fit only into a corner, so that it is not feasible to reorient them to face straight down the room. However, in some cases it is possible to position just the mid-range and tweeter components to face straight down, or it may be necessary to remove these components from the original cabinet and place them in a small enclosure atop the cabinet to permit the desired orientation.

When corner speakers are used as in Fig. 911, the listener close to one of the side walls is likely to enjoy the stereo sensation even though he hears substantially more sound from one speaker system than from the other because of his location. This is because he receives a full share of the high-frequency content of the program material. Definition, one of the important attributes of the stereo sensation, can be achieved by receiving two versions of the same sound, from the left and the right, as in the case of the listener midway between the two speaker systems and by effective reproduction of the transients, which give a sound its character. The latter requires full high-frequency response, and the listener near the side wall obtains such response when the treble speakers are placed as in Fig. 911.

The foregoing discussion does not necessarily represent all views on stereo speaker placement. Moreover, the views presented

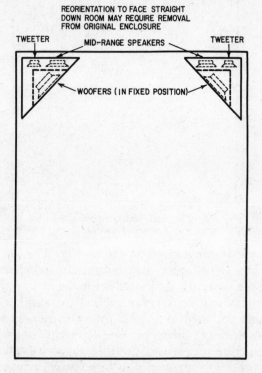

Fig. 911. *Reorientation of the mid-range speakers and tweeters to improve the stereo effect when corner speakers are used.*

do not necessarily apply to all circumstances. No two listening rooms have quite the same acoustics, and it is quite possible that a speaker placement which is ideal for one room will not be satisfactory for another, even though both may have similar dimensions. Room furnishings, location of doors and windows, height of ceiling, material of walls, floor and ceiling, etc. affect acoustics. The only safe guide is experimentation. True, it is not very easy to experiment with the location and spacing of two speaker systems, particularly if they tend to be large. However, high-quality speaker systems in modest-size packages are available to facilitate the stereophile's task.

One speaker system (Fig. 912) consists of a woofer in fixed position, as usual, while the mid-range and tweeter units are mounted, not on the front cabinet panel, but on a swivel chassis so that they can be pointed in the desired direction. Fig. 913 shows several ways in which one might employ this arrangement.

Fig. 912. *A fixed woofer is often used in conjunction with mid-range and tweeter units, such as those shown. to produce the stereo illusion.* (Courtesy Jensen Mfg. Co.)

Speaker quality

Originally it was thought by some that the stereo illusion masked distortion, uneven frequency response, inadequate bass or treble response and other deficiencies. Extensive listening, however, has proven the opposite. High-quality speakers are just as necessary for stereo as for monophonic reproduction. A leading manufacturer has stated:

"It has been held by some workers in this field that many of the offensive effects of distortion are eliminated in stereo systems. This we do not believe to be the case. Conclusions such as those just cited are drawn because the spaciousness and directive qualities of stereo are such an improvement over low-quality mono sources that many of the flaws are overlooked; thus listening fatigue, which is developed subconsciously, is just as likely with low-quality speakers in stereo as in mono. The difference is primarily in incubation time."[1]

Another prominent speaker manufacturer has stated:

"It is just as important to use high-quality units with a stereo system as it is with any single-source installation. But quality, of course, is not determined by price alone, and the buyer must carefully choose speakers which match his listening preferences and particular room acoustics."[2]

Thus, a heavily draped and carpeted room with much upholstered furniture will tend to absorb highs; therefore speaker systems which emphasize the treble range may be best suited to such a room.

Some authorities have stated that speaker systems which divide the audio spectrum among as many as three or four loud-speakers are not always productive of the best stereo sound. In such systems the separation between speaker units may be a substantial number of inches or even a matter of feet. While this may be fine for monophonic reproduction, providing an impression of a broad source of sound, stereo on the other hand often seems to work best when the sound sources at the left and right are narrow—well focused—rather than diffused. In other words, it is claimed, each speaker system should provide "integrated" rather than spread-out sound, leaving it for the stereo method—namely the use of two (or more) speaker systems —to achieve the illusion of spatial distribution.

Speaker matching

It is quite well agreed that matched speaker systems are neces-sary to realize fully the potential of stereo, although varying de-grees of emphasis are placed upon this requirement. One manu-facturer has stated the case for matching:

"We attach considerable importance to the use of matched speakers primarily because this is one of the big factors in pro-ducing a good center. This is self-evident since the sound that appears to emanate from the center is produced when the two sources are in perfect balance. The balance must be, not only in intensity on an overall basis, but at every individual frequency."[3]

Another speaker manufacturer has said:

"In true stereo reproduction, we feel that consistently good per-formance can be achieved only with closely matched speaker

---

[1] Correspondence from James B. Lansing Sound, Inc.
[2] Correspondence from R. T. Bozak Sales Company.
[3] Bozak, *op. cit.*

systems. The idea that one speaker system may reproduce brasses best, while another is perfect for bass viols, is valid, but there is no way to guarantee that the recording engineer had the peculiarities of such a combination in mind when he made the recording. Some material will sound excellent on such a mismatched arrangement, but most of it will be degraded."[4]

At the extreme are those who claim that matching is not only a matter of buying speakers of the same brand and model but also of selecting speaker units of identical characteristics, in the same way that one might purchase matched tubes for the output stage of a power amplifier. A music editor of a leading recording company claims he finds the stereo effect varies significantly according to which pair of speakers he is using, even though all are of the same brand and model. While it is doubtful that more than a few stereophiles will have access to a group of speakers from which they can pick the two that seem best matched, one can approxi-

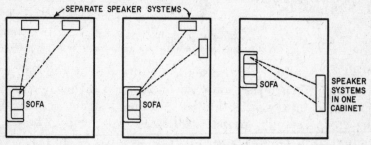

Fig. 913. *Several ways in which the system shown in Fig. 912 can be used.*

mate this situation by buying high-quality speaker systems made under close tolerances and tight standards of inspection so as to be relatively uniform from one unit to the next.

Representing a more moderate view, one speaker manufacturer has stated:

"Identical speakers are not required. However, both speakers should be good ones . . . It goes without saying that the treble ranges of both speakers should be of equal quality, although not precisely identical."[5]

Presumably the manufacturer has in mind such factors as smoothness of response, distortion and the radiation pattern when he refers to equal quality.

---

[4] Lansing, *op. cit.*

[5] Electro-Voice, Inc., "Application of Electro-Voice Speaker Systems to Stereo Reproduction," *Technical Bulletin No. 1.*

If the speaker systems are mismatched in terms of frequency response, some sounds may wander from left to right or vice versa (Fig. 914). Here the left speaker is assumed to have relatively flat response, while the right speaker is assumed to have a peak in the region of 500 cycles and a dip at 3,000 cycles. Suppose a violin is playing a note with a dominant frequency of about 500 cycles and that the sound of the violin is supposed to issue principally from the left speaker. However, the peak of the right speaker will cause it to produce an undue proportion of notes in the vicinity

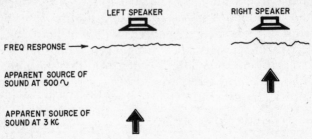

Fig. 914. *An apparent shift in the sound source will occur if unmatched speakers are used.*

of 500 cycles, which may cause the violin apparently to shift from left to right. When the violin plays a lower or higher note, it will apparently shift back to the left. Another instrument, playing a tone predominantly around 3,000 cycles, may seem to be on the left instead of on the right, where it belongs, because the right speaker exhibits a dip in response in the 3,000-cycle region (Fig. 914).

Phasing

To achieve the illusion of sound emanating, not only from the left and the right, but also from the area midway between the two speaker systems, and to prevent partial cancellation of sound, especially at low frequencies, it is necessary that the two speaker systems operate in phase. Accordingly, there should be ready provision for changing the phase of one of the channels by 180°. Some stereo control amplifiers and integrated amplifiers make such provision. If not, a phasing switch (Fig. 820 in the preceding chapter) can be easily installed between one of the power amplifiers and the speaker system; some speaker systems incorporate such a switch. By feeding the same sound to both channels at equal levels, one can tell whether phasing is correct if the sound appears to issue from a point midway between the two speakers.

If phasing is incorrect, the sound will appear to have an indefinite origin.

In a number of speakers, with stereo in mind, the polarity of their terminals is shown. If a small battery is connected in the same manner to each speaker, the moving element will in both cases move in the same direction. This may be referred to as battery phasing.

But battery phasing does not always correspond to true phasing. Should one of the channels on the program material accidentally be out of phase, then the speakers will correspondingly be out of phase. If dissimilar power amplifiers, or perhaps dissimilar control amplifiers, are used, although the incoming signals may be in phase, the outgoing signals may be out of phase because of differences in the design (number of stages) of the two amplifiers. Therefore, it would be necessary to correct the out-of-phase signal condition by reversing the leads to one of the speaker systems, even though this is contradictory to battery phasing.

When in-phase signals are fed to the speakers, there is still a possibility that out-of-phase connections to one of the speakers may produce best results. This can happen if the two speakers are at substantially different distances from one's customary listening position, as illustrated in Fig. 913. In such a case, the phase of some frequencies arriving from the left speaker will be appreciably different from the phase of the same frequencies arriving from the right speaker. Which frequencies are involved depends upon the difference in distance from the listener to each speaker. Only experiment can determine whether true phasing or reverse phasing will provide better results under such circumstances. If reverse phasing sounds better, it will usually do so only in a limited area.

Speaker level

With monophonic systems many audiophiles have sought to approach realism by reproducing music at towering volume, sometimes louder *to the ear* than the original sound. High volume simulates reality by raising all sounds well above the noise level of the room, by defining each instrument or each voice, by bringing up the apparent balance of the bass frequencies with the rest of the audio spectrum (Fletcher-Munson effect), and perhaps by setting up additional reverberation in the listening room.

In stereo, opinion is somewhat mixed as to the volume level required for realism, although most recommendations are for a playback level similar to that of the original sound. One authority has stated:

> "One advantage that stereo sound does offer over monaural [monophonic] sound is that loudness is not nearly as critical for faithful reproduction. Thus stereo need not be played as loud as monaural for complete musical satisfaction."[6]

However, this does not necessarily mean that substantially reduced levels in stereo will maintain the illusion of reality. It simply holds that stereo need not be played as loud as monophonic, which is often reproduced *above* the level of the original sound (to the ear).

A more positive case for high-level stereo reproduction has been made:

> ". . . the [stereo] effect is sufficiently arresting to supply some of the 'oomph' which some people try to supply in ordinary systems by boosting the level of reproduction. It is certainly true that with stereo program material it is no longer necessary to boost the intensity *above* live concert level to hear fine details. But with stereo we feel it even more desirable that material be played at a natural listening level. Most listeners seem to feel that as volume is reduced, the realistic quality vanishes even more quickly than with single-channel reproduction. Some stereo recordings of symphonic works sound very much like single-channel material until they are played *very* loud, and then suddenly the whole orchestra opens up and the effect is magnificent."[7]

A balance between woofer and tweeter levels satisfactory for monophonic reproduction may not be so for stereo. Specifically, a higher tweeter level may be better. This is particularly likely to be true if the speakers are angled so that the high frequencies to a substantial extent bounce off the walls instead of reaching the listener directly. Accordingly, one speaker manufacturer has made this recommendation with respect to use of its speaker systems for stereo:

> "The settings on the treble and very-high-frequency attenuators . . . should be advanced to the full 'on' position for stereo reproduction. This is necessary for the preservation of bass–high balance, due to inordinate absorption of the highs by the walls' reflecting."[8]

Because of the role played by the upper frequencies in the

---

[6] Bozak, *op. cit.*

[7] Lansing, *op. cit.*

[8] Electro-Voice, *op. cit.*

stereo effect, the user may find it desirable deliberately to increase their level relative to the nondirectional bass notes as a means of accentuating the stereo effect.

Phantom-channel speaker

Some stereo control amplifiers provide a phantom-channel (center) signal by mixing the left and right signals and making the resultant available at a third output jack. To take advantage of this, a third power amplifier and a third speaker system are necessary. However, it is possible to save the cost of a third power amplifier by connecting the center speaker system to the left and right power amplifiers. Fig. 915 shows one of the popularly recommended methods of connecting them. However, this procedure causes some crosstalk. The center speaker acts as a link between the left and right amplifiers, so that a certain amount of the left signal reaches the right speaker, and vice versa. However, the indications are that the isolation between channels is well over 20 db, probably closer to 30 db, and therefore quite satisfactory for stereo.

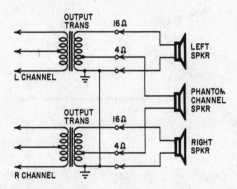

Fig. 915. *Method of connecting a phantom-channel speaker.*

This method, assuming that all three speaker systems have the same efficiency, results in the center speaker having an acoustic output lower than each of the flanking speakers. Whether this is a desirable relationship between phantom and outer channels is open to question. In any event, the user does not have a ready means for varying the respective levels. If each speaker were independently fed by a power amplifier, one could use the input level controls of the amplifiers to adjust relative levels or, in some cases, the control amplifier may have a gain control for the phantom channel. L-pads can be installed in the speaker systems to adjust their levels. But the ability of a power amplifier to damp the speaker may be limited by an L-pad to such an extent that noticeable hangover (resonance) will occur at low frequencies, causing the bass to be less clean and the sound as a whole to be "muddy." This depends upon the speaker system employed.

The method of Fig. 915 raises the problem of signal cancellation. Assume there are equal signals in the left and right channels. This can happen, depending upon microphone techniques. There would then be no electrical potential between the

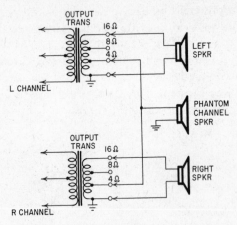

Fig. 916. *Alternative method of connecting a phantom-channel speaker to two stereo power amplifiers.*

4-ohm terminals (or any other pair of like terminals), and therefore no signal. However, in actual stereo program material, there are generally differences in amplitude and phase between like signals, so that signal potentials will exist between like terminals. But this does not mean that *no* cancellation takes place. To prevent any cancellation that might occur, an alternative technique is to connect the middle speaker to the outputs in parallel (Fig. 916). But the disadvantage here is that crosstalk is appreciably greater than in the case of Fig. 915. Isolation between the left and right channels is then likely to be somewhat less than 20 db, which is basically a serious situation, although how serious depends upon the nature of the program material and the extent that one counts upon left–right separation for stereo effect.

Assuming that the level of the center speaker can be adjusted relative to that of the flanking speakers, what should this relationship be? Authoritative opinions are mixed, so that the best answer for the present is that the stereophile should find out for himself through experiment. However, the views of the experts may serve to some extent as a guide.

Paul W. Klipsch has concluded that the middle speaker's output should be 3 db higher than *each* of the flanking speakers. In other words, the middle speaker's output should be equal to the *combined* output of the other two. Klipsch has written:

"Some guessing was done as to the level to be fed the center channel, and the guesses were all wrong. Experiment led to better

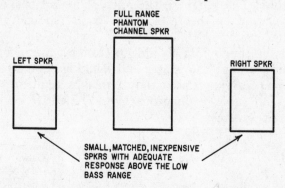

Fig. 917. *A limited-cost stereo speaker installation incorporating a phantom channel.*

thinking, and a theoretical basis was arrived at and corroborated. . . . My experiments resulted in a workable system with the center channel a half-and-half mixture of the two sound tracks, (from a tape), and the flanking channels using corner speakers fed from the two sound tracks with 3-db attenuation relative to the center channel . . . When success finally was achieved in balance, a surprise occurred: the center channel was perfectly real, and not just a simulated effect to fill up a hole in space. Sounds remembered as arising in the center of the stage occurred there; one ceased to hear sounds from the three speakers, and actually sensed a spread across the curtain of sound."[9]

Others have recommended that the center-channel level should be *lower* than the end channels:

"The gain of the center channel should be adjusted so that the sound from the center speaker is just audible."[10]

[9] Paul W. Klipsch, "Two-Track, Three-Channel Stereo," *Audiocraft*, November, 1957.
[10] Correspondence from D. R. von Recklinghausen, chief research engineer, H. H. Scott, Inc.

Another has recommended that the center channel should be 6 db below each end channel.[11]

Possibly the discrepancy in views as to the proper level of the phantom channel relative to the other two may be explained by variations in speaker location or by the nature of the program material. For example, if very wide microphone spacing were used in the original recording, it might be desirable to compensate for the excessive difference between the left and right signals by elevating the volume of the center channel. Or, if the left and right speakers are far enough apart to form an angle considerably more than 40° with the listener, it may be desirable to accentuate the center channel. The narrower the microphone or speaker spacing, the lower should be the level of the center speaker relative to those at the ends.

In sum, the stereophile should not commit himself to a fixed relationship between the center and flanking speakers but leave the way open for experimentation, either by acquiring a control amplifier with suitable phantom-channel facilities or by L-pads in his speaker systems.

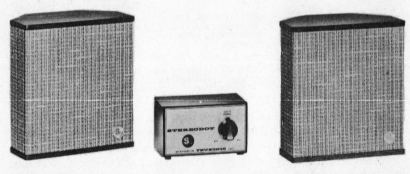

Fig. 918. *This system is designed to be used with a full-range speaker. The two small enclosures contain 8-inch speakers which receive the left and right signals respectively. The crossover supplies the full-range unit with the combined signals.* (Courtesy Stephens Tru-Sonic, Inc.)

Although use of the phantom channel appears to increase the cost of a stereo system because it requires a third speaker; and perhaps a third power amplifier as well, actually it may cost no more or even less than a two-speaker setup, at the same time affording high-quality reproduction and solving the problem of space for many a prospective stereophile. How this can come about is indicated by Fig. 917.

Here the center speaker system is an expensive one and, as

---

[11] Correspondence from Leonard Feldman, president, Madison Fielding.

frequently happens with expensive systems, a large one. Quite possibly, the center speaker is the one hitherto used by the listener for mono reproduction. Instead of having to find the funds and space for a matching speaker system, he can employ small, matched, relatively inexpensive speakers for the left and right

Fig. 919. *An internal view of the Stereon. This horn-loaded unit is designed for use with a full-range speaker system.* (Courtesy Electro-Voice, Inc.)

channels. The center speaker provides the total audio information, particularly the low bass, which is essentially nondirectional and not substantially associated with the stereo effect. The flanking speakers, being small and inexpensive, do their relative best in the upper bass, middle and treble ranges, which are most closely associated with the stereo effect. The cost of the two small speaker systems for the left and right may be considerably less than the cost of matching an existing mono speaker system. Or, if one is starting fresh, the cost of a full-range speaker system, plus two small systems effectively covering from about 200 or 300 cycles upward, can be appreciably less than the cost of two full-range speaker systems. Really good bass reproduction is quite expensive, and by limiting such reproduction to one speaker system, a considerable saving is possible.

Fig. 918 shows a commercial version of Fig. 917. Known as the Stereodot, it is intended for use with any full-range speaker.

It consists of two 8-inch speakers, each in a very small enclosure, together with a crossover network, which is connected to the left and right power amplifiers. The crossover feeds the combined left and right signals to the center speaker. It feeds the left-channel frequencies above 400 cycles to the left speaker, and the right channel frequencies above 400 cycles to the right one.

Limited-range stereo speakers

Low bass frequencies need not be reproduced by both speaker

Fig. 920. *The Stereon in use. The slim compact unit is the limited range system which produces the stereo effect.* (Courtesy Electro-Voice, Inc.)

systems because of the nondirectional characteristics of the low notes. Accordingly, there are some two-speaker systems which employ a limited-range speaker for one of the channels.

One of these, called the Stereon, is shown in Fig. 919. Fig. 920 shows the Stereon in use with a full range speaker system. It consists of one limited-range speaker plus a crossover network, which is attached to the two power amplifiers. Through the crossover, the Stereon speaker receives only frequencies above 300 cycles in one of the channels, say the left. The full-range speaker receives not only all the frequencies in the right channel, but also the bass frequencies in the left channel.

The Stereodot system, already described, also comes under the heading of a limited-range speaker system. In each case a special

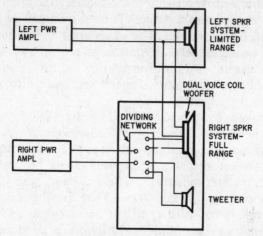

Fig. 921. *A stereo speaker system using a dual voice-coil woofer.*

crossover restricts the range of frequencies handled by one of the speakers, and at the same time transfers those frequencies which have been eliminated—the bass notes—to another speaker system, which handles the bass of both channels.

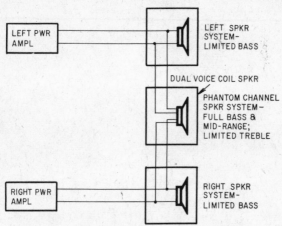

Fig. 922. *A dual voice-coil woofer is used for the phantom channel in this system.*

Another system (Fig. 921) similar in principle but different in method uses one limited-range speaker system (say the left) plus one full-range speaker system (the right). In this case, the full-range system employs a special woofer with two independent voice coils that drive the one cone. As shown in Fig. 921, one of the voice coils receives the left-channel signal while the other receives the right-channel signal. Thus the bass of both channels is reproduced by the woofer. Use of separate coils on one speaker isolates the two channels. Inasmuch as the woofer has a sharp drop in response above a few hundred cycles, the middle and high frequencies of the left channel are not reproduced to a significant extent by the right speaker.

The dual-voice-coil speaker can also be used in a phantom-channel configuration, as in Fig. 922. Speakers are also manufactured with response extending well into the treble range, so that the center speaker comes a good deal closer to providing true phantom-channel reproduction. The situation here is much like the Stereodot setup of Fig. 918. That is, the center speaker approaches full range, with excellent bass coverage, while the end speakers reproduce the middle and high notes adequately but fall off in the low bass region as the usual result of using small speakers in conventional small, simple enclosures.

installing a stereo system

WE have dealt with the recording, broadcasting and microphone techniques employed for conveying stereo information, and also with the fundamental elements of an audio chain, as shown in Fig. 1001—the program sources (disc, tape, radio broadcast), the signal sources (phono cartridge, tape head

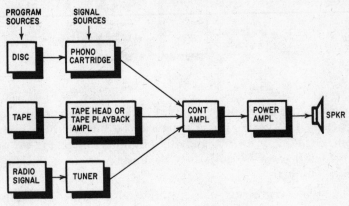

Fig. 1001. *Basic elements of an audio chain used in a monophonic system.*

or tape amplifier, tuner, microphone), the control and power amplifiers, and the speakers. It is now time to consider the various problems of bringing these elements together to produce a working, satisfying stereo system.

199

Integrated vs separate components

Thinking for the moment in terms of a monophonic system, the electronic components can be purchased separately or in various combinations. Thus one can buy a tuner, control amplifier and power amplifier separately, or a tuner–control-amplifier combination, or a control-amplifier–power-amplifier combination, or a tuner–control-amplifier–power-amplifier all on one chassis.

In stereo, the possible combinations are even more numerous.

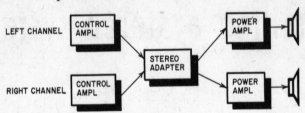

Fig. 1002. *A stereo system which consists entirely of separate components.*

Fig. 1002 illustrates the amplifier portion of a stereo system consisting entirely of separate components. There are two control amplifiers, a stereo adapter to coordinate them, and two power amplifiers. The adapter is shown following the control amplifiers.

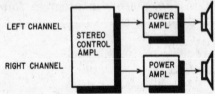

Fig. 1003. *This system uses separate power amplifiers fed by a stereo control amplifier.*

However, if the amplifiers contain a tape-monitor switch, as explained in Chapter 8, the adapter can be inserted at a point between the selector switch and the volume control for minimum distortion because it will then deal with low-level rather than high-level signals.

Fig. 1003 represents a step toward integrated components. There is a stereo control amplifier, which eliminates the need for an adapter, and there are two power amplifiers. Fig. 1004 illustrates an integrated stereo preamplifier. A further step toward integration combines a stereo control amplifier and a stereo power amplifier (Fig. 1005).

A different step toward integration is that of Fig. 1006, which

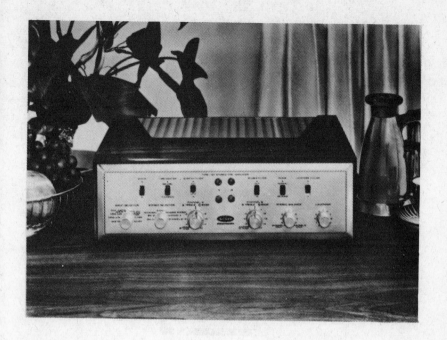

Fig. 1004. *A stereo control amplifier which contains facilities for handling all types of program material.* (Courtesy H. H. Scott, Inc.)

shows two integrated monophonic amplifiers (control-amplifier–power-amplifier combinations) linked by a stereo adapter. This is feasible if the amplifiers contain a tape-monitor switch to permit insertion of the adapter at a point before the power amplifier section. If no such switch is provided, it is necessary to make

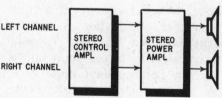

Fig. 1005. *A stereo amplifier system which uses a stereo control amplifier and a stereo power amplifier.*

changes (usually fairly simple) in the integrated amplifiers to permit insertion of the adapter at a point between the selector switch and the volume control.

Finally, Fig. 1007 shows a complete stereo amplifier, with all control and power amplifier facilities incorporated on one chassis.

Each approach to a stereo installation has merits and disadvantages. What is best depends very much upon the individual in question—upon the relative importance of being economical, the amount of space available for mounting components, the equipment already owned, the special features necessary for individual needs or preferences, the acuity of the listener's ear and

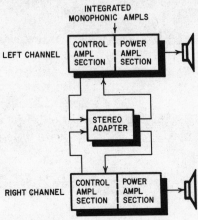

Fig. 1006. *This system features two integrated monophonic amplifiers connected to a stereo adapter.*

upon his standards of performance. Therefore we will not attempt a net evaluation as to which approach is the best.

Judging from experience with monophonic equipment, the highest quality has been found in separate components. This does not mean that a control amplifier appearing as an individual unit is necessarily better than the equivalent section of a control-amplifier–power-amplifier combination. But characteristically, the separate component has been superior. Apparently, the manufacturer who concentrates his forces upon one component at a time comes up with a better, albeit more expensive, product. When two or more components are brought together on one chassis, some compromises are usually made in the interest of conserving space or funds, or sacrifices are made in terms of features and flexibility.

To illustrate: a first-class control amplifier may be as large, although not as heavy, as some integrated amplifiers (control-amplifier–power-amplifier combinations). The size of the former will be due to such factors as affording generous ventilation, using oversize components for long life (oil-filled capacitors, a relatively large power transformer that runs cool, high-wattage resistors, high-voltage capacitors), ample spacing between circuit elements to avoid hum pickup or feedback (which may cause oscillation), and the incorporation of extra features. Similarly, a high-quality power amplifier may be built along the same rugged, space-consuming lines. Combining two such units results in an integrated amplifier of such massive proportions that compromise is called for to make the unit's size acceptable to the purchaser.

This does not mean that the performance of an integrated unit is likely to fall below high-fidelity standards. Such standards encompass a *range* of performance instead of denoting a fixed level. The likelihood is that the separate component will come closer to the top of the range than the integrated unit. For many individuals, the difference between the two will be inaudible or unimportant.

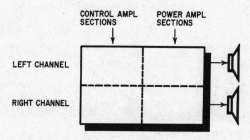

Fig. 1007. *A fully integrated stereo amplifier.*

The integrated stereo amplifier has the following specific advantages: It is more economical, occupies substantially less space, incorporates matched components, reduces the number of connecting cables between elements of the stereo system, is simpler to operate because all controls are on one panel, and is less expensive to use because it draws less total power than equivalent separate components. Typical integrated stereo amplifiers are shown in Fig. 1008. When combined with a suitable speaker system these amplifiers, along with suitable program sources, comprise complete stereo systems.

By using separate components, one *may* achieve greater flexibility through a greater number of desired operating features. Another advantage is that if trouble occurs in one component, the entire amplifier system does not have to go to the service technician. Instead, part of the system can continue to render monophonic service. Moreover, when trouble arises, one can substitute components to ascertain where the trouble lies. For example, if

Fig. 1008. *This integrated stereo amplifier features pancake construction.* (Courtesy Sherwood Electronic Labs., Inc.)

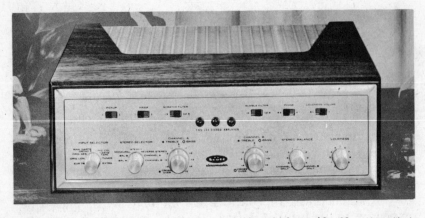

Fig. 1008 (continued). *An integrated stereo amplifier which provides 20 watts output on each channel.* (Courtesy H. H. Scott, Inc.)

one channel goes dead, the owner can substitute components from the other channel one at a time to determine whether the fault lies in the control amplifier, power amplifier, connection to the speaker or elsewhere.

Use of separate components enables the owner of a monophonic system, particularly expensive high-quality equipment, to convert to stereo without discarding at great loss what he already has.

Finally, the use of power amplifiers separate from the control amplifiers permits ready balancing of one channel against the other to compensate for differences in efficiency between the stereo speakers; where separate power amplifiers are employed, they ordinarily incorporate level sets that permit such adjustment.

Integrated speakers

The question of integrated vs separate components applies to speakers and other elements of the stereo system as well as to the amplifier section. Several manufacturers have developed integrated stereo speaker systems; that is, two systems in one cabinet. For the sake of clarity, we shall refer to these as dual-speaker systems inasmuch as the term integrated speaker system has another meaning, as we shall soon see.

Various, and for most part ingenious, principles have been employed to incorporate two speaker systems in one cabinet and yet preserve the stereo effect. In the majority of instances, results are commendable. Nevertheless, it continues to be true that greatest satisfaction is likely to be derived from separate systems, enabling the experimentally inclined listener to try various spacings between speakers, various locations in the room and different degrees of angular placement with respect to the listener.

On the other hand, whether all this experimental effort is worth while depends very much upon the individual. For many, the increase in satisfaction obtained through an experimentally achieved placement as compared with the results from a dual speaker system may be insignificant. For others, the additional effort and expense may be rewarding. The individual most exhilarated by directional effects may gain something through the additional spacing permitted by separate speakers. Yet another listener may be disturbed by such spacing—he may find the fusion achieved through the relatively close spacing of a dual speaker system more pleasing.

The term integrated speaker system is also used in another sense, to denote that the speaker and its cabinet are made and sold as a unit. Integration can be even further extended. Fig. 1009 illustrates a stereo system that is completely integrated inasmuch as the cabinetry and electronic components were designed to complement each other.

As a general rule, the chances of obtaining a high-quality speaker system with the requisite smoothness and low distortion —even more important for stereo than for monophonic reproduction—are greatest when the enclosure and speaker are designed for each other. If one buys just the speaker and then encloses it in a cabinet purchased from another manufacturer, in a built-to-

Fig. 1009. *In this installation integration has been carried to the point where the cabinetry has been designed for the equipment used.* (Courtesy Bell Sound Systems Inc.)

order cabinet or in an enclosure of one's own construction, the results may well be just the opposite of what one hopes for.

Much art and science are involved in matching the speaker and enclosure, and the chances of the individual without technical resources and equipment achieving a satisfactory match are relatively small. This is all the more true when high-quality results are sought from speaker systems occupying a small space. The greatest difficulties are apt to arise with respect to bass response, but at the same time poor effects may occur in any other part of the audio range.

Many things may go wrong when the individual purchases the speaker separately from the enclosure: Resonances of the woofer and enclosure may fail to complement each other in the manner required for smooth, extended low-frequency response. If one attempts to construct a horn enclosure, it may be insufficiently airtight for proper operation. Inadequate padding may result in insufficient absorption of mid-range frequencies, causing ragged response due to sound bouncing around within the enclosure, so that some frequencies are reinforced and others are partially cancelled. Speaker buzzes or rattles may become apparent only when the speaker is mounted in the enclosure, or the enclosure may rattle because of improper construction. If the speaker is firmly bolted to a warped panel, this may warp the speaker and cause distorted sound. Dividing networks, especially if constructed by the individual, may depart excessively from correct value, producing unbalanced frequency response. Where different speakers are used for different parts of the audio range, phasing between speakers may be incorrect, causing a "hole" in response to the crossover region (at frequencies where the output of both speakers is supposed to be equal). The kind of tweeter chosen, or its angle of orientation, may cause excessive beaming of high frequencies, with inadequate high-frequency response if the listener is but slightly out of line with the axis of the tweeter; the directional aspect of stereo may suffer greatly thereby. The woofer may be insufficiently damped in a given enclosure, resulting in muddy bass. The tweeter, if mounted in the same enclosure as the woofer, may be adversely affected by radiation from the back of the woofer. The levels of the woofer and tweeter may be incorrectly balanced with respect to each other. And so forth.

Integrated tuners

The design and construction of an FM tuner are rather critical if it is to be a high-quality unit with good sensitivity, freedom from oscillation and drift, low distortion, sharp selectivity and wide frequency response. Accordingly, the very best units tend to be those in which the manufacturer has concentrated on the FM tuner design to the exclusion of other possible components in combination with the tuner, such as a control amplifier or AM tuner.

A number of quite satisfactory combinations, such as an FM tuner and an AM tuner on one chassis, are to be found. For those within normal listening range of FM stations, the differences between average and the best high-fidelity FM tuners tend to be little if at all perceptible, although they may be measurable. The advantages of economy, compactness and having all controls on one panel will in many cases make an FM–AM stereo tuner a more desirable purchase than separate FM and AM tuners, even though the latter have an edge in quality of performance.

Integrated tape machine

For the stereophile planning to include commercial prerecorded stereo tapes as a program source, a considerable saving is possible in that he can purchase a tape transport without accompanying tape electronics (tape amplifier). The transport's function is to move the tape from a supply reel, past the heads and onto a takeup reel. The signals from the stereo tape head can be fed directly into the stereo control amplifier (or integrated amplifier); it is virtually universal practice to incorporate suitable amplification and equalization for such signals in these units. Thus the control amplifier has input jacks marked "tape head."

A substantially more expensive alternative is to purchase the tape electronic components, either separately or as an integral part of the transport. We shall assume that the electronics are integral in the sense of having been designed specifically for the transport in question; physically, the two may or may not be separate.

In deciding whether to purchase just the transport or an integrated tape machine, the following factors must be considered:

1. Does the control amplifier (or integrated amplifier) provide accurate tape equalization? Most commercial tapes recorded at 7.5 ips require NARTB equalization and the trend is to employ it for 3.75-ips tapes too.

2. High-frequency response differs among heads, depending principally on the width of the gap—the narrower the gap, the better the treble response. In an integrated machine, the playback amplifiers generally take account of this factor, and the equalization is tailored to compensate for the particular heads used. The control amplifier with tape-head facilities must assume either ideal tape-head response or a given amount of departure from the ideal. While the error in equalization due to varying gap-width loss among heads is apt to be relatively small at 7.5 ips, it can be appreciable at 3.75 ips, where preservation of high-frequency response is a more severe problem.

3. The cable length from the playback head to the control amplifier must be the shortest possible to minimize high-frequency losses. Furthermore, the cable must be carefully routed to avoid hum pickup. The signal produced by the playback head is extremely small and undergoes a tremendous amount of amplification, particularly at the lower frequencies. Hence, a very slight pickup of hum by the cable will become audible. In an integrated tape machine, the problems of cable length and routing are generally solved by the manufacturer.

4. The two sections of a stereo tape head may differ somewhat in output for the same amount of signal on the tape. If the control amplifier contains level sets for the tape-head input, this difference can be compensated for. If there are no such controls, or if the level sets have been pre-empted for similar use in connection with the magnetic phono input, it is possible to compensate for the differences between tape-head sections by means of the gain controls of the integrated tape machine.

5. Even though the stereophile initially plans to play only pre-recorded tapes, recording facilities may eventually prove highly desirable. Control amplifiers, although they contain the electronics needed for tape-head playback, do not contain the circuits required for recording because the latter are a good deal more complex. For recording, an oscillator is required to supply high-frequency bias current to the record head (to reduce distortion and increase the amount of signal recorded on the tape) and to energize the erase head. A record-level indicator (meter, magic-eye tube or neon lamp) is necessary to indicate whether the recording level is too high (causing excessive distortion), too low (causing a poor signal-to-noise ratio) or about right. Accordingly, one cannot expect an already complex stereo amplifier also to include tape recording electronics.

Consequently, the individual must decide beforehand if he plans eventually to get into recording; if the answer is affirmative, he has to purchase recording units along with the tape transport. This additional expense is justified when we remember that there is the possibility of making live stereo recordings with a pair of microphones. Also one can make stereo tapes off the air and there is a good point to making tapes from stereo discs. A tape can be played thousands of times without suffering damage, such as the scratches and graver disasters that often befall discs, and without significantly changing with respect to frequency response, noise and distortion. The stereo disc tends to be more delicate than its monophonic counterpart; its more complex groove structure is easily altered by the stylus, particularly if stylus pressure is not kept at the minimum permissible for good performance. It has been noted that crosstalk and distortion tend to increase, and high-frequency response to decrease, after a number of plays of a stereo disc. Accordingly, it makes sense to play the stereo disc once to record a tape, and then put the disc aside, playing the tape as often as wished. In the case of accident to the tape, the disc can be brought out again for making a new tape (the old one can be erased).

Installation

If a stereo installation is to operate properly in an electrical sense, it must be placed properly in a physical sense, with due attention to ventilation, neat and careful arrangement of cables, and accessibility for adjustments, checking and servicing. Because of the complexity and number of components in a stereo system, the physical installation has to be even more painstaking than that of a monophonic system. Of course it is also nice to have an installation that is attractive in appearance.

With four power output tubes operating (unless a simplex power amplifier, described in Chapter 8, is used), which are capable of producing from 20 to 120 watts of power, a considerable amount of heat is generated. To this is added the heat from other amplifier tubes, particularly rectifiers, and from the other electronic components, such as control amplifiers, tuners and tape amplifiers. Therefore the installation must provide air vents at least above and behind the components to permit dissipation of the heat. In addition, vents at the sides, bottom and front are desirable if feasible. The nearest surface above the electronic components should be at least 6 inches away. If this surface is capable of charring, an asbestos shield may be advisable where minimum space is available.

When the units are installed and first turned on, observe them during their first hour of operation for undue heat buildup. The danger is not particularly that of fire but of injury to the components. Overheating will substantially shorten the life of the tubes and possibly damage other parts, such as resistors and capacitors, resulting in malfunction—distortion, noise, incorrect frequency response, etc.

Considering that in stereo there is essentially two of everything —whether integrated or not—and taking into account the number of components that go into an audio system, there is considerable likelihood of a "rat's nest" of wiring developing unless care and patience are used in making an orderly arrangement of the connecting cables. Neatness is desirable not merely for its own sake but to prevent possible malfunction and to facilitate checking and servicing components.

Cables carrying low-level signals—from a phono cartridge or from a tape head—must be kept away from cables carrying high-level signals, such as those leading from control amplifiers to power amplifiers. If a low-level and a high-level cable of different channels come too close, there is a possibility of crosstalk; that is, the signal in the latter cable may be picked up by the former. Also if low- and high-level cables of the same channel are near each other, there is a possibility of feedback and consequent oscillation.

Fig. 1010. *The problems of heat and wiring can be solved by using an open installation of the type shown.* (Courtesy H. H. Scott, Inc.)

To avoid hum pickup, cables must be routed as far as possible from transformers and motors (phono turntable and tape transport). While this applies especially to low-level cables, it is also true for high-level ones. More than once, an elusive hum problem has been traced to the routing of high-level cables.

To help arrange cables in proper fashion, one may use hooks, clamps and similar devices attached to cabinet shelves or walls. If staples are employed, make sure that they do not cut into the cables. It is worth while to identify each cable by attaching a label, using adhesive tape or similar means.

In planning his stereo installation, the owner must give careful thought to accessibility and ease of removal of *all* components. Tucking away a power amplifier in a hard-to-reach spot is not a good idea. Easy access is desirable for adjustment of rear

211

panel controls for servicing and for the periodic checkup that high-fidelity equipment should receive by way of preventive maintenance. One way to solve the problems of heat, accessibility and cable length is to provide an open installation of the type shown in Fig. 1010. The modern approach to external design of audio components makes installations of this type possible.

Balancing procedure

Close balance between speaker levels—within 2 db or less, according to expert opinion—is necessary for best stereo performance. (Balance does not necessarily mean that the left and right speakers produce equal sound levels. Rather, it means that the relationship between levels at the left and at the right is the same in reproduction as at the original performance.) In Chapter 8, part of the discussion of stereo amplifiers was based on the balance control as a means of equating sound levels. That discussion also dealt with other amplifier facilities that may be useful for balancing purposes, such as level sets and certain stereo switching arrangements. It remains, then, to present a specific balancing procedure.

To provide a frame of reference for the balancing procedure, it is advisable (1) to review and elaborate upon the various factors that can produce imbalance in a stereo system; (2) to list the amplifier and other facilities that can be employed for achieving balance; (3) to state some guiding principles.

Sources of imbalance are:

1. The program sources—disc, tape, radio broadcast. Several db difference may exist between the two channels on these stereo media.

2. The signal sources—phono cartridge, tape head or tape amplifier, tuner. To illustrate, one section of a stereo cartridge may have 6-db more output than the other section, although the recorded signals on the stereo disc are equal in each channel. The same is more or less true for a stereo tape head. Two tuners employed to receive a stereocast will probably differ in sensitivity.

3. The control amplifiers. Although matched components are employed for stereo, such as two control amplifiers on one chassis, nevertheless there may be small imbalances between the two channels due to parts tolerances.

4. The power amplifiers. The comment in point 3 applies here.

5. The speakers. Speakers of identical brand and model tend to vary in efficiency by a few db. (However, some manufacturers

produce closely matched speakers through rigorous manufacturing practices and quality control.)

6. The master gain control. Its tracking error—variation in level *between* channels as the control is rotated—will vary from a few db in some amplifiers to as much as 10 db in others.

If matched components are not employed in the case of control amplifiers, power amplifiers and speakers, then the imbalances can become quite profound instead of being a matter of only several db.

The facilities for correcting imbalance are:

1. The balance control. Not all stereo amplifiers contain this device. Instead, some provide individual gain controls for each channel, usually concentrically mounted and with a push-pull locking device so that the two can be operated as one whenever desired (thus serving as a master gain control). While the following discussion is in terms of a balance control, it also applies in essence to those situations where separate controls are employed for adjusting balance.

2. Input level sets on the control amplifier and on the power amplifier. In an integrated amplifier, the only level sets available are, of course, those of the control amplifier section.

3. Gain control on stereo tuners and on tape amplifiers.

To provide a readily identifiable reference point, balance among the stereo components should occur when the balance control is at mid-setting—the knob pointing to 12 o'clock. (In the case of separate gain controls, balance should occur when both controls are at the same degree of rotation, as indicated by marks on their respective knobs.) One may temporarily depart from this reference point to achieve a desired effect, but you can always return to it to get your bearings. Achieving balance among components at mid-setting of the balance control affords equal reserve in either direction for correcting other imbalances. To illustrate, if the balance control has to be turned almost fully clockwise to achieve balance, there might not be adequate reserve to correct a severe inequality between channel levels on a stereo disc or tape.

The foregoing requirements lead to an important rule: Before resorting to the balance control, balance between components must be achieved by whatever other means are available. The essential task of the balance control will then be to compensate for imbalance due to either (1) inequality between channel levels in the program source (disc, tape, stereocast) or (2) tracking error of the master gain control.

The stereo balancing procedure may be divided into four steps:

1. First, the balance control is turned to mid-position, the reference point. Since rotation of the master gain control is apt to upset balance between channels, this control is turned to the normal listening position (ideally about 12 o'clock to 2 o'clock), which is noted as a reference point. With the balance control at mid-position and the master gain control at normal position, *equal* signals should enter each channel of the stereo system from disc, tape or radio so that equal sound levels from the stereo speakers result.

2. The second step is to furnish the *same* signal (not half of a stereo program) to each channel of the signal source; that is, to the stereo cartridge, stereo tape head or stereo tuner. A monophonic disc is a ready means of feeding identical signals, equal in frequency content and level, to each section of a stereo cartridge. In the case of a stereo tape head, test tapes are available that alternately furnish the same signal to each section of the head. Or one could use a full-track monophonic tape. Another course is to run a roll of erased tape from reel to reel, with the tape machine in playback position, and hold a bar magnet firmly against the traveling tape. This will cause a substantial amount of noise to appear on the full width of the tape; the noise may then be used as the signal to be presented to each section of the head. (After the tape has served its purpose, apply a head demagnetizer to the heads to remove magnetization resulting from the dc signal on the tape.)

In the case of an FM and AM tuner pair employed for receiving stereocasts, the procedure is to tune each one to a monophonic program broadcast by the same FM–AM station that transmits stereo material. If one listens to more than one such station, balance should be obtained with respect to the station that is tuned in most frequently for stereo. Adjustments for other stations, assuming that balance between the FM and AM tuners changes with station, can be made with the balance control or with the volume control of one of the tuners (the one with the highest level).

3. The next step is to provide for rapidly switching between two conditions: left channel on and right channel off, or left channel off and right channel on. This enables one to compare the sound level of each speaker when reproducing the same

signal. Some stereo amplifiers contain a switching arrangement that permits listening to either channel L on its own speaker or channel R on its own speaker. Others do not. In the latter case, the listener can easily install a switch such as was shown in Fig. 809, allowing him to alternate the sounds of the two speakers. For accurate comparison of the speakers' sound levels, the listener must be equi-distant from each speaker. To minimize error, the speakers can be temporarily positioned next to each other.

4. The final step is to adjust level sets (on the control amplifier or power amplifier or integrated amplifier) and volume controls (on the tuners and tape playback amplifier) to achieve acoustic balance while switching between the speakers. Generally, distortion is least when the signal is reduced at an early stage in the audio system. Therefore, if one has a choice between using the level set of a control amplifier or of a power amplifier to achieve balance, it is usually preferable to employ the former. (On the other hand, turning down the level set of a power amplifier has the advantage of reducing noise in the control amplifier produced after the gain control.)

Depending upon the control amplifier or integrated amplifier that is used, there may be level sets for some signal sources but not for others. The procedure would be to balance first the signal source for which there is no level set; if no other means of adjustment is available, use the balance control. The resultant setting of the balance control becomes the reference point. Leaving the balance control in this position, one then balances the sources for which there are level sets. To illustrate, a stereo integrated amplifier made by one manufacturer contains input level sets only for a stereo tape amplifier and for the tuners. None are provided for magnetic phono. Since this is an integrated amplifier, no power-amplifier level sets are available. Therefore one has to achieve balance on the phono signal by means of the balance control. Leaving the balance control at this setting, one would then equate the signals from the stereo tape machine using the level sets on the integrated amplifier; and one would do the same with respect to the signals from the tuners.

Occasionally, the only available level sets are those of the power amplifiers. The procedure might then be as follows: First, use these level sets to equate the magnetic phono signals, with the balance control at mid-position. Second, adjust the tuners by means of their respective volume controls, taking note of the positions which achieve balance. Third, equate the tape machine's signals by means of the latter's volume controls, again taking note of the positions corresponding to balance. If the tape signals are obtained directly from the playback head, these signals would have to be adjusted through the balance control, taking note of the position where balance is effected.

It may be that no level sets are available. In this situation one has to rely on the balance control for each signal source, noting in each case the position of the control. For the source most frequently used, for example phono, it may be worth while to remove the balance-control knob and replace it so it points to 12 o'clock when balance is obtained, even though the shaft of the control is not at mid-setting. Hence the easily remembered 12-o'clock position will denote balance for phono signals; however, it will not be possible to turn the control equal amounts to the left and right.

Balancing for phantom-channel output

Some stereo control amplifiers have a phantom-channel output jack, which supplies equal proportions of the left and right signals.

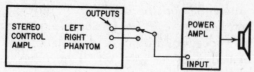

Fig. 1011. *A method of balancing the output signals of a stereo control amplifier.*

Consequently, the balancing procedure must see to it that equal signals are present at the control amplifier's left and right output jacks, from which points the phantom signal is obtained.

One can employ a meter to check the control amplifier's left and right output jacks. If a meter is not available, the ear is a suitable measuring instrument. This entails connecting *one* power-amplifier–speaker combination alternately to the left and right output jacks of the control amplifier, as in Fig. 1011. Some stereo control amplifiers contain switching facilities for this purpose. Otherwise, the listener must improvise. After it has been ascertained that equal signals emanate from these jacks, the power amplifiers and speakers are reconnected in normal stereo fashion. Then, adjust the input level sets of the power amplifiers to obtain balance for the system as a whole, using the switching arrangement of Fig. 809 or amplifier facilities to alternate the sounds of the two speakers.

Balancing for program source inequalities

Where the two channels of the program source are of unequal level, compensate by turning the balance control from its reference position. Use the amplifier switching facilities or else the arrangement of Fig. 809 for alternating the sound between the two speakers until the ear is satisfied that balance exists.

Balancing for tracking error

Once the stereo system has been balanced with the master gain control in normal listening position, invest some time in learning what happens to the balance as the master gain control is turned up and down. Note the adjustments of the balance control required to restore signal equality at various settings of the master gain control.

Balancing for listening position

It is debatable whether one should adjust the balance control to compensate for a listening position that is not approximately equidistant from each speaker. One point of view is that if one moves away from an equidistant listening point, this corresponds to sitting at the left or right instead of at the center of a concert hall (or other site), and therefore one should not tamper with the balance. The other view is that a listener at the left of a concert hall might gain greater enjoyment if the members of the orchestra on the right side played somewhat louder. The balance control enables one to approximate an effect of this sort.

Phasing

An important step in making a stereo installation is phasing the two speaker systems. The subject has already received full treatment in Chapters 8 and 9, and the reader is referred to those discussions.

Minimizing noise and distortion

The level sets on the control amplifier and power amplifier are useful not only for balancing purposes but also, as in a monophonic installation, for minimizing noise and distortion. Reduction of noise and distortion takes on added importance in stereo because they tend not only to be offensive in themselves but also to disrupt the stereo illusion.

The control amplifier level sets enable one to prevent high-level signal sources (piezoelectric phono cartridge, tuner, tape amplifier, TV) from overloading the control amplifier in the event the signal goes through one or more tube stages before reaching the volume control. Similarly, they prevent the signal from the preamplifier (for magnetic phono cartridge, tape head and microphone) from overloading the following stage.

The input level set of the power amplifier can be used to cut down the noise from the control amplifier. (It may be added, parenthetically, that this level set also enables one to prevent the power amplifier from being driven to levels sufficient to damage the speaker.)

The objective is to turn down the power amplifier level set to reduce control-amplifier noise generated after the volume control. However, this means that the control amplifier must produce a higher signal to begin with, which may entail a significant increase in distortion. Accordingly, in turning down the power amplifier level set, ascertain—using the evidence of your ears—that the control amplifier does not work so much harder that distortion increases perceptibly. The problem is not critical in a high-quality control amplifier, which can turn out from 2 to 4 volts at imperceptible distortion, whereas the power amplifier (and in turn the speaker) usually can be adequately driven by anywhere from 0.1 to 0.5 volt.